My Weird School Special

Deck the Halls, We're Off the Walls!

Dan Gutman

Pictures by
Jim Paillot

SCHOLASTIC INC.

To my Facebook fans

ISBN 978-0-545-64012-1

Text copyright © 2013 by Dan Gutman. Illustrations copyright © 2013 by Jim Paillot.
All rights reserved. Published by Scholastic Inc., 557 Broadway, New York, NY 10012,
by arrangement with HarperCollins Children's Books, a division of
HarperCollins Publishers. SCHOLASTIC and associated logos are trademarks and/or
registered trademarks of Scholastic Inc.

12 11 10 9 8   13 14 15 16 17 18/0

Printed in the U.S.A.   40

First Scholastic printing, December 2013

Typography by Kate Engbring

Contents

The Best Christmas Vacation!

My name is A.J., and I hate it when a song gets stuck in my head.

Does that ever happen to you? You hear a song a couple of times and learn the words without even trying. Then you find yourself singing it *all* the time. You sing it while you're walking to school. You sing it while you're taking a bath. You can't stop singing it no matter where you are.

I *hate* when that happens!

Ever since Thanksgiving they've been playing this rap song on the radio over and over again. I can't get it out of my head.

The song is by this kid who isn't much older than me. His name is Johnny Cray, but his rap name is Cray-Z. My sister loves him. Every girl in the *world* loves him.

The song is called "The Christmas Klepto." It's about this mean guy who steals toys. It starts like this. . . .

'Twas the night before Christmas.
You know the rest.
Stuff was all over; the house was all messed.

I was dreaming of a Christmas white.
It was a totally silent night.

That's when I heard a crash and a boom,
So I ran right down to the living room.

There was this guy dressed all in black,
And over his shoulder he carried a sack.

I took one look at him and said, "Whoa, man!
I know you're not Frosty the Snowman."

"Who are you?" I asked after a pause.
"You sure don't look like Santa Claus."

He said, "The name's Klepto. I'm from
the South Pole.
I grab all your presents. That's how I roll.

"On Christmas Eve, I go around the world
and steal all the presents from boys and
girls."

Ugh. That song is the worst part about
Christmas. And now it's stuck in my head
forever.

Do you know what's the *best* part about Christmas? No school for nine whole days! That's right. No homework. No reading, writing, math, or social studies. No teachers.

Yippee!

Nine days! Do you know how long nine days is? I figured it out on my calculator. Nine days is the same as 216 hours. 216 hours is the same as 12,960 minutes. 12,960 minutes is the same as 777,600 seconds. That's a *long* time.

For 777,600 seconds I won't have to see Andrea Young, this annoying girl in my class with curly brown hair.

I'm going to enjoy every one of those seconds. This is going to be the greatest Christmas vacation of my life.

The First Rule of Being a Kid

I was eating breakfast when the greatest Christmas vacation of my life got even *greater.* My mom was sitting at the table reading her newspaper when I saw this on the back page. . . .

SANTA CLAUS IS COMING TO TOWN!

I leaned forward so I could read the small letters. They said that Santa was going to be at our local shopping mall on Saturday, just before Christmas.

All my dreams had come true!

If you ask me, Santa Claus is the greatest

man in the history of the world. Anybody who gives toys to kids should get the No Bell Prize. But I figure Santa will never get the No Bell Prize, because that's a prize they give out to people who don't have bells. And if there's one thing Santa has plenty of, it's bells.

"Can you take me to the mall on Saturday?" I asked my mom. "Please, please, *please*?"

"Dad and I need to clean out the garage on Saturday," my mom replied.

"You can clean out the garage *anytime*, Mom," I told her. "Santa is only going to be at the mall on Saturday. If I don't go, I'll never get to see him for the rest of my *life*."

"Sorry, A.J. Not this Saturday."

"But I need to buy a present for Amy," I begged.

My sister, Amy, is three years older than me. She's annoying, but I have to get her a present anyway.

"No," Mom said. "No means *no*."

Hmmm. Begging usually works for me. I would have to try something else. If at first you don't succeed, try, try again. That's what my parents always say. You can accomplish *anything* if you put your mind to it.

It was time to put Plan B into effect.

I started crying.

If you want something really badly and

the situation is hopeless, there's only one thing to do—cry. That's the first rule of being a kid.

I peeked to see if my mom was watching me cry.

"A.J.," she said. "Those are crocodile tears."

What do crocodiles have to do with anything?

"Come on, Mom!" I pleaded. "I've been waiting to meet Santa Claus my whole life."

Mom put down her newspaper and looked at me. She had a serious look on her face.

"Your father and I have been meaning to tell you something for a while now, A.J.,"

she said. "It's about Santa Claus. We think it's time you knew that Santa—"

But she didn't get the chance to finish her sentence because the phone rang. I picked it up.

It was my friend Ryan, who will eat anything, even stuff that isn't food.

"Santa is coming to the mall!" Ryan

shouted into the phone.

"I know!" I shouted back. "Do you think it's the *real* Santa? I mean, how could he visit every mall in the world?"

"He's not visiting every mall in the world," Ryan told me. "He's just visiting *our* mall! That's why we have to be there. Are you in? My mom said she would drive us. Spread the word."

I hung up and called my friends Michael, Neil, and Alexia to tell them the big news about Santa.

"I want to go!" said Michael, who never ties his shoes.

"I want to go!" said Neil, who we call the nude kid even though he wears clothes.

"I want to go!" said Alexia, who rides a skateboard all the time.

In case you were wondering, everybody was saying they wanted to go.

I looked at my mom with my best puppy dog eyes. If you ever want something really badly, look at your parents with puppy dog eyes. That's the first rule of being a kid.

"Please?" I asked. "Ryan's mom said she'd drive us to the mall. You don't even have to go."

"You'll buy a present for your sister while you're there?" Mom asked.

"Of course!"

"Okay," my mom agreed. "You can go."

Yippee!

A Christmas Miracle

I had to wait a million hundred hours for Saturday to arrive. Wednesday felt like it was two days long. Thursday must have been three days long. Friday took at least a week. I thought I was gonna die of old age.

But finally, it was Saturday. My mom

made me wear the dorky red-and-green Christmas sweater that my aunt knitted for me last year. Ugh, it's itchy.

"Do I *have* to wear this?" I asked.

"Yes," my mom replied. "You want to look your best in front of Santa."

"I don't want to look like a dork in front of Santa," I said.

"You look very handsome, A.J."

When I came downstairs, my sister, Amy, was watching TV in the living room.

"Nice sweater, dork," she told me.

I didn't care what Amy said. It would be worth it to wear a dorky, itchy sweater if I could see Santa Claus live and in person.

I sat in the window for a million hundred minutes waiting for my ride. Finally, Ryan's minivan pulled up.* Ryan, Michael,

---

* I think it's called a minivan because it was invented by some lady named Minnie.

Neil, and Alexia were inside. They were all wearing their itchy Christmas sweaters.

"Nice sweaters, dorks," I said as I climbed in.

Lots of people had decorated their front yards for Christmas. We drove past

giant inflatable snowmen, candy canes, Santas, sleighs, and lots of reindeer. It was beautiful. Ryan's mom started to sing *"I'm dreaming of a white Christmas . . ."* and we all joined in.

That's when the most amazing thing in the history of the world happened.

It started to snow!

Well, that may not be all that amazing to *you*. But we live in California, and it hardly *ever* snows here.

"It's snowing!" we all marveled as we pressed our noses against the windows.

It was a Christmas miracle.

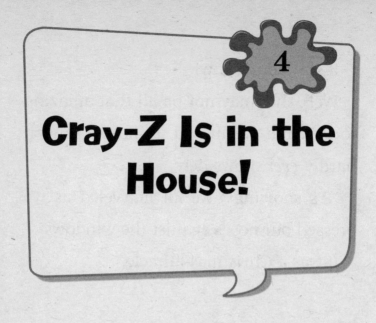

Cray-Z Is in the House!

When we got to the mall, the parking lot was jammed. Ryan's mom circled around trying to find a spot.

"Everybody must be here to see Santa," she said.

"I wonder where he parked his sleigh," Michael said, looking around.

"Santa doesn't park his sleigh in a parking lot, dumbhead," said Neil the nude kid. "That would be *crazy*."

"Where do you think he parked it?" asked Alexia.

"Up on the roof, of course," said Neil.

Right next to the mall entrance was a big bus. On the side of bus, in big red letters, it said: CHRISTMAS RAPPIN' WITH CRAY-Z.

"Cray-Z is here!" shouted Alexia. "That must be his tour bus!"

"Cray-Z?" asked Ryan's mom. "Who's Cray-Z?"

Ryan's mom is really old, so she doesn't know anything. We had to tell her that

Cray-Z is this kid rapper, and his song "The Christmas Klepto" is on the radio all the time.

"Do you like his music?" Ryan's mom asked us.

"Ugh, no!" said Ryan.

"That kid is horrible," said Michael.

"I call him Justin Timberfake," said Neil.

We all said how much we couldn't stand Cray-Z's music. I didn't tell anyone that Cray-Z's dumb song had been stuck in my head all week.

Suddenly, a bunch of girls came running out of the mall. They surrounded the bus.

"We love Cray-Z!" they were shouting. "Marry me, Cray-Z!"

Those girls were screaming and crying

and fainting all over the place. What is their problem?

"Girls are weird," said Alexia, who is technically a girl but likes cool boy stuff anyway.

Finally, Ryan's mom found a parking spot. We had to walk a million hundred miles to get to the entrance of the mall.

"WOW!" we all said, which is "MOM" upside down.

When we walked through the door,

everything was *Christmas-y*. There were candy canes, wreaths, colored lights, jingle bells, and huge paper snowflakes all over the place. **MEET SANTA TODAY** said a banner on the wall. I could hear "Rudolph the Red Nosed Reindeer" playing. Big Christmas ornaments were hanging from the upper level of the mall. Zillions of people were walking around. There was electricity in the air!

Well, not really. If there was electricity in the air, we would get electrocuted.

"You're big kids now," Ryan's mom told us as she took a cell phone out of her pocketbook. "I'm going to do some Christmas shopping. We can stay in touch by phone."

She gave Ryan the cell phone and told him to put it in his pocket.

Cell phones are cool. My mom said I could get one when I'm in high school.

"We'll meet at the food court in two

hours," Ryan's mom told us. "I need you kids to stay together and be careful. Don't get into trouble, do you hear me?"

"*Us* get into trouble?" I asked.

"What could possibly happen?" asked Alexia.

"We *never* get into trouble," said Michael.

Ryan's mom looked at us with those crazy grown-up eyes that make it seem like she's drilling an invisible hole in your head. Then she left.

The mall is big. Right in the middle is a *ginormous* Christmas tree that almost reaches the ceiling. How they got that tree in the mall, I'll never know.

We walked all over the place looking for Santa.

"I'm glad Andrea and Emily aren't here," said Alexia. "They're so annoying."

"Hey, I have an idea," I said. "Let's use Ryan's cell phone and make a prank call to Andrea's house."

Everybody agreed that was a genius idea, so I should make the call. Ryan speed-dialed the number for Andrea's house.

"Hello?" somebody answered.

I wasn't sure if it was Andrea or her mother.

"I would like to order a large pepperoni pizza," I said.

"You must have the wrong number. This is not a pizza parlor."

The gang was cracking up. It was

definitely Andrea's mother on the phone.

"Do you have ravioli?" I asked.

"No!"

"How about spaghetti?"

"No!" Andrea's mother said. "Wait a minute. Is this A.J.? Are you calling for Andrea? She's not home. She's at the—"

I didn't hear the end of the sentence, because that's when the most amazing thing in the history of the world happened.

Somebody tapped me on the shoulder. But I'm not going to tell you who it was.

Okay, okay, I'll tell you. But you have to read the next chapter. So nah-nah-nah boo-boo on you.

True Love

5

"Hi Arlo!"

"Ahhhhhhhhhhhhhhhh!"

It was Andrea! She's the only person in the world who calls me by my real name.*

I must have jumped three feet in the air. Little Miss Perfect was with her crybaby

---

* Because she knows I don't like it.

friend Emily. They were carrying a bunch of packages.

"What are *you* doing here?" I asked Andrea. "Buying yourself a new encyclopedia because your old one wore out?"

"Very funny," said Andrea. "Emily and I bought toys for homeless girls and boys."

"That's right," said Emily, who always agrees with everything Andrea says. "We want to bring peace and harmony to kids all over the world."

"Oh, yeah? Well, we came to meet Santa Claus," Alexia said.

"*Oooooo!*" Andrea said, all excited. "We want to meet Santa, *too*. Can we come with you guys?"

"We'll have to talk it over," I said.

The gang and I moved off to the side and huddled up like football players.

"What do you think?" asked Neil. "Should we let them hang out with us?"

"I say no," I said. "I don't want to walk around with Andrea all day."

"*Oooooo*, A.J. doesn't want to walk with

Andrea," said Ryan. "They must be in *love*!"

"Wait a minute!" I yelled. "I told you I *didn't* want to walk with Andrea. Why are you saying I'm in love with her?"

"A.J., everybody knows you love Andrea," said Neil. "It's totally obvious that you only said you didn't want to walk with her to hide the fact that you're in love with her."

Hmmmmm.

"Okay," I said, "in that case, it's okay with me if Andrea walks with us."

"*Oooooo*, A.J. wants to walk with Andrea!" said Ryan. "They must be in *love*!"

"Wait a minute! That's not fair!" I shouted. "So it doesn't matter *what* I say. I'm in love with Andrea whether I want to walk with her or not."

"*Oooooo*, A.J. just admitted he's in love with Andrea!" said Alexia.

"When are you gonna get married?" asked Neil.

If these kids weren't my best friends, I would hate them.

Waiting in Line Stinks

Andrea said she knew where Santa was, and she led us to the other side of the mall. Finally, we found the end of the line of people waiting to meet Santa. There must have been a million hundred kids there! I could see a sign in the distance that said **SANTA'S WORKSHOP**, but Santa Claus was too far away. He was in a special roped-off area.

"We should sneak up to the front of the line," I whispered.

"That would be wrong, Arlo," Andrea said. "These kids got here before we did."

I was going to sneak up anyway, but a big arm came down in front of my face. I looked up. You'll never believe whose arm it was.

Officer Spence, our school security guard! He was standing on a Segway. Those things are cool.

"Officer Spence!" I said. "What are *you* doing here?"

"Making sure everybody waits in line,"

he told me. "And earning a little extra money over the holidays."

"How long will we have to wait in line?" Ryan asked.

"About an hour," Officer Spence said.

"An *hour*?!"

"We could die from old age while we're waiting," I said.

"An hour is like forever,"

said Michael.

Andrea rolled her eyes. "Boys should learn to be patient," she said.

I wasn't sure if it was worth it to wait in line for an hour. I thought that maybe we should just forget about meeting Santa. But that's when I heard these magic words. . . .

"Santa is giving out candy," some kid said.

"Santa is giving out candy,"

said some other kid.

"Santa is giving out candy!" said another kid.

In case you were wondering, everybody was saying that Santa was giving out candy. And if there's one thing that I love almost as much as Santa, it's *candy*. All the candy I got on Halloween was gone.

So we decided to stay in line.

But waiting in lines is boring. To kill the time, I practiced what I was going to say when I got to Santa. . . .

"I want the new Striker Smith Commando action figure with missile launcher, voice activator, attack dog, and deluxe blowtorch. Other accessories sold separately. Batteries not included."

Striker Smith is a superhero from the future who travels through time and fights all who dare to thwart his destiny. He can turn into a jet plane when you push a button on his stomach. His armor suit is tough enough to withstand a nuclear blast. He's a one-man wrecking machine, ready to take on any evil to save the world.

Two Christmases ago, I got my first Striker Smith action figure. Then on the school bus I tied a string to Striker's leg and lowered him out the window so he could fight bad guys who were attacking the bus. But Striker fell under the bus and got decapitated. That's a fancy way of saying his head came off. We had a funeral for his head.*

I got a *new* Striker Smith last Christmas. But he met his untimely end when his head got tragically melted in a battle

---

* I wrote this poem in his honor: *Ashes to ashes, dust to dusted. / We buried Striker because he was busted. / He was cool, but now he's dead. / It's hard to live without a head.*

with an evil magnifying glass. So now I wanted to get a new Striker, the one that comes with a blowtorch. It is cool.

Most of the other kids in line were little. They didn't even look like they were in first grade yet. Man, I thought, those kids can't even *read*. They don't know what two plus two equals! They don't know *anything*. It's hard to believe that I was that dumb just a few years ago.

Standing still is the most boring thing in the history of the world. What a snoozefest. The line inched forward a little. I could almost see Santa.

"I bet it's not the *real* Santa," I told Alexia. "It's just some guy in a Santa suit."

The little kid in front of me heard that

and turned around. He was holding his mother's hand, and he looked like he was going to cry. He must have been waiting for a long time already. If these kids didn't get to meet Santa soon, they were going to freak out.

A group of grown-ups strolled by the line singing Christmas carols. Somebody else walked by with a real reindeer. There were more reindeer in a petting zoo.

"Where do you think they got those reindeer?" Michael asked me.

"From Rent-A-Reindeer," I told him. "You can rent anything."

Some lady came by asking kids if they wanted to write a letter to Santa and have it delivered to the North Pole. That was a dumb idea. Santa was right here at the mall. Why would I want to send a letter all the way to the North Pole?

"When are we going to get there?" asked Ryan.

"Waiting in line stinks," I said.

"You boys are annoying," Andrea said. "Why don't you go take a walk? Emily and I will hold your place in line."

She didn't have to ask us twice. We got out of there.

7

A Present for My Sister

"Let's go to Candy Castle!" Ryan shouted as soon as we got out of the line.

"Let's go to Cinnabon," shouted Michael.

"Let's get ice cream!" said Neil the nude kid.

"Let's go to the skateboard shop!" said Alexia.

Malls are cool. There's so much stuff to see and do, especially around Christmastime. Our mall even has a *train* in it.

We ran over to the train. It goes around and around in circles on metal tracks. At the ticket booth was an elf with a funny hat and pointy ears, like on *Star Trek*. The elf turned around, and you'll never believe who it was.

Mrs. Kormel, our bus driver!

"Mrs. Kormel!" I shouted. "What are *you* doing here?"

"Bingle boo!" she said. "I'm running the train . . . and earning a little extra money over the holidays."

"Aren't you a little tall to be an elf?" asked Alexia.

"Elves come in all sizes," Mrs. Kormel told us. "All aboard! *Toot toot!*"

That train ride looked lame, so we didn't get on. Any train that needs an elf to toot for it must be lame.

We ran over to the escalator. Escalators are cooler than trains, and you don't need tickets to ride them. My friend Billy, who lives around the corner, told me that if you run down an up escalator for ten seconds, you'll travel back in time.*

Neil said he had to go to the bathroom, so we went over to the men's room and waited for him to finish. That's when I remembered that my mom gave me money to buy a present for my sister. I didn't know what to get her. What do you get for an annoying sister?

"You're a girl," I said to Alexia. "What do *you* think my sister would like? Perfume? Jewelry?"

---

* That works with revolving doors, too.

"Why don't you get her a new skateboard?" suggested Alexia. "That's what I want."

A *skateboard*!

"My sister doesn't even know how to ride a skateboard," I told Alexia. "Why would she want that?"

"No, that's a *great* idea, A.J.!" said Ryan. "Buy your sister a skateboard. Then when she doesn't use it, the skateboard is yours."

"That's *genius*!" I said.

Alexia and Ryan should be in the gifted and talented program.

Neil came out of the bathroom. We were about to go over to the skateboard shop to buy my sister's present when the most amazing thing in the history of the world happened.

It started with a noise—a high-pitched *screech*. At first it was far away. Then it got louder.

And louder.

There was the thunder of feet. They were getting closer.

And closer.

Then there was screaming!

Then we saw a bunch of girls running in our direction. There must have been five hundred of them.

"EEEEEEEEK!" one of them screamed. "I think I see Cray-Z!"

"I love you, Cray-Z!"

Cray-Z was running right at us, and he was being chased by a thundering herd of screaming girls.

"In here!" I yelled to him. "Follow me!"

Ryan, Michael, Neil, and Alexia formed a human wall to stop the girls. I hustled Cray-Z into the men's bathroom. He was gasping for breath. I thought he was gonna die.

He put his hand on my shoulder and looked me in the eye.

"You gotta help me, dude," he said. "Those girls are *nuts*!"

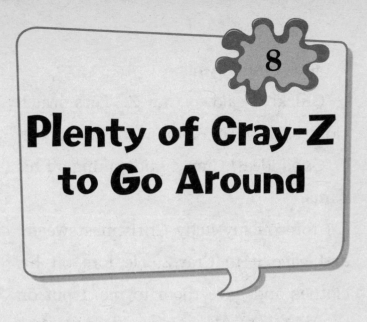

Plenty of Cray-Z to Go Around

The famous Cray-Z was standing right next to me, live and in person!

"I can't take it anymore!" Cray-Z moaned. "They're gonna tear me apart! I need somewhere to hide!"

I didn't know what to say. I didn't know what to do. I had to think fast.

So I did the first thing that came to my mind.

I took off my pants.

"Quick!" I said to Cray-Z. "Let's switch clothes! They'll never know the difference!"

"Good idea!" Cray-Z said, taking off his pants.

I tore off my itchy Christmas sweater and gave it to Cray-Z. He tore off his clothes and gave them to me. I put on his clothes and he put on mine. I looked pretty sharp with his hat and sunglasses. It was hilarious.

"Do I look like you?" I asked him.

"Yeah," he said. "Do I look like *you*?"

"Yeah," I said. "You chill in here for a while. I'll take care of your fans for you."

I pulled the hat down low over my

face, strolled out of the men's room, and
gave a big wave to the girls. They started
screaming and pulling out cameras to
take my picture.

"Look, it's him! It's Cray-Z!"

"I love you!"

"Can I have your autograph?"

Those girls were totally buying it! They
really thought I was Cray-Z!

"Sure you can have my autograph," I said.

The girls started sticking pens and paper in my face. I wrote CRAY-Z as fast as my hand could move.

"One at a time, girls," I said cheerfully. "One at a time. There's plenty of Cray-Z to go around."

"EEEEEEK! I touched him!" a little girl screamed. "I'll never wash this hand again!"

After they got my autograph, girls were fainting, crying, and freaking out all over the place. They didn't know that I was just a regular kid. They had no idea that the *real* Cray-Z was hiding in the bathroom.

It was cool to be a famous celebrity. This

was the greatest day of my life!

But you'll never believe who rolled over on his Segway at that moment.

It was Officer Spence, the mall security guard!

Uh-oh. The jig was up. I figured I was in *big* trouble.

"I'm sorry, Mr. Z," said Officer Spence, "but it's time."

"Time for what?" I asked.

"Time for you to sing."

"Huh? What? M-me?" I stammered. "Nobody told me—"

"Hurry up!" Officer Spence said. "They're all waiting for you."

"Who all? Huh? Where?"

Officer Spence grabbed my hand and pulled me up on his Segway. We rolled over to a stage that had been set up near the center of the mall. There were four musicians on the stage wearing Santa hats.

"Get up there!" yelled Officer Spence.

I climbed up on the stage.

"Yo, Z," said the guitar player. "You the man."

The girls started screaming. I looked

out at the sea of faces. Some of these fans were younger than me. Some of them were older than me. A few of them looked like my grandma! That was weird. I gave a little wave, and they all started freaking out like they never saw a guy wave before. A guy in a jacket and tie climbed onto the stage and picked up the microphone.

"Okay, boys and girls," he said. "This is the moment you've all been waiting for. Here's the latest pop sensation to sing 'The Christmas Klepto,' his new hit song . . . *Craaaaaaaaaaaay-Zeeeee!*"

The girls screamed even louder. The musicians started playing that annoying song. I had no choice. I grabbed the mic and started rapping. . . .

"'Twas the night before Christmas.
You know the rest.
Stuff was all over; the house was all messed.

I was dreaming of a Christmas white.
It was a totally silent night.

That's when I heard a crash and a boom,
So I ran right down to the living room.

There was this guy dressed all in black,
And over his shoulder he carried a sack.

I took one look at him and said, 'Whoa, man!
I know you're not Frosty the Snowman.'

'Who are you?' I asked after a pause.
'You sure don't look like Santa Claus.'

He said, 'The name's Klepto. I'm from the
South Pole.
I grab all your presents. That's how I roll.

'On Christmas Eve I go around the world
and steal all the presents from boys and girls.'"

You know what? Those girls were
digging it! You should have *been* there!
The best part was, they were screaming
so loud that nobody could tell I wasn't the
real Cray-Z. So I kept rapping. . . .

"He went to the corner and got down on one knee
To scoop up the gifts that were under our tree.

He took them all. He grabbed my new toys.
He took my new clothes. He took all our joy.
To the Christmas Klepto, everything's free.
'I'll take your partridge,' he said, 'and your pear tree.

'I like your presents, and now they're mine.
Say, how much of this stuff did you buy online?

'You better watch out. You better not cry.
You make one peep, and I'll poke out
your eye.'

'You're a mean man, sir!' I said with a hiss.
Just wait until Santa finds out about this.'"

I didn't get to finish the song because that guy in the jacket and tie hopped up on the stage again and grabbed the mic away from me.

"Isn't Cray-Z fantastic?" he yelled. "He'll be back at two o'clock to sing for you some more."

The girls screamed. Officer Spence grabbed my hand. I hopped on his

Segway, and he took me back to the men's bathroom.

In the bathroom, Cray-Z was looking in the mirror and combing his hair. When he saw me, he turned around and gave me a hug.

"You saved my life, dude!" he told me. "I owe you one, big-time."

Take a Chill Pill

When I came out of the bathroom wearing my regular clothes, the whole gang clapped me on the back.

"You were *awesome*, A.J.!" said Alexia.

"Those girls didn't suspect a thing," said Ryan.

"How did you know the words to that dumb song?" asked Michael.

"It's been stuck in my head all week!" I admitted.

We hustled through the crowd to get back to Santa's Workshop, all the way at the other end of the mall. It took a long time to find Andrea and Emily. They were close to the front of the line now.

"Where *were* you?" Andrea asked with her mean face on. "What took you so long?"

"It's almost our turn to meet Santa!" said Emily.

"Take a chill pill," I told them. "We're here, right?"

I could see Santa Claus now. He was sitting on this big throne with his red suit, red hat, white beard, and black boots—the whole getup. Santa was fat and jolly, just like I imagined. He was surrounded by Christmas trees, presents, fake snow, and a giant nutcracker on each side.*

"Ho! Ho! Ho!" Santa bellowed.

"Y'know, I'm not sure that's the real Santa," said Neil the nude kid.

"It looks like Santa to me," said Michael.

"I'm so excited!" said Andrea, rubbing her hands together.

Soon it would be our turn. We were on

---

* Man, there must be some big nuts if they need such big nutcrackers.

pins and needles.

Well, not really. We were just standing there. If we were on pins and needles, it would have hurt.

I got up on my tiptoes to look all around. There were so many happy, smiling faces. Christmas trees. Twinkling lights. Jingle bells jingling. It was a beautiful scene.

"Ah," I said, "I love the smell of tinsel at Christmastime."

"Tinsel doesn't smell, dumbhead," said Andrea. "That's pine needles that you smell."

"It's your *face* that I smell," I said.

Why can't a truck full of tinsel fall on Andrea's head?

Just then, one of Santa's elves came running down the line of kids. "It's almost your turn to meet Santa!" she said.

That's when I realized that the elf wasn't a real elf. It was our librarian, Mrs. Roopy! She was dressed up like an elf!

"Mrs. Roopy!" I said. "What are *you* doing here?"

"Who's Mrs. Roopy?" asked Mrs. Roopy. "I'm one of Santa's helpers from the North Pole."

She wasn't fooling anybody. It was Mrs. Roopy for sure. That's when I realized that *all* of Santa's helpers were grown-ups from our school. The guy playing Christmas songs on the organ was our music teacher, Mr. Loring. The lady dressed up like Frosty the Snowman was our custodian, Miss Lazar. Another one of the elves was our Spanish teacher, Miss Holly.

"Miss Holly!" I said when I saw her. "What are *you* doing here?"

"Earning a little extra money over the holidays," she said. "We all are. *¡Feliz Navidad!*"

"I guess teachers don't get paid very much," said Ryan.

"Teachers get paid?" I asked. "I thought they just came to school every day because they had no place else to go."

There was just one family in front of us in line now. A lady with a big camera came over. I did a double take. The lady was Ms. Hannah, our art teacher!

"Merry Christmas!" she said. "Now listen up. When you sit on Santa's lap, I'm going to snap your picture. So let's see some big smiles, okay?"

"Okay!" we all said.

"Do you want to buy the twenty-dollar package or the forty-dollar package?" Ms. Hannah asked us.

"Package of *what*?" I said.

"Package of pictures, of course," said Ms. Hannah. "The twenty-dollar package includes one eight-by-ten in a nice frame. The forty-dollar package includes *two* framed eight-by-tens and ten wallet-size pictures. I suggest you buy the forty-dollar package so you can share your pictures with your grandparents, your aunts, your uncles. . . ."

What a scam.

"I don't want to buy *any* package," I

told Ms. Hannah.

"Yeah," said Alexia. "We just want to meet Santa."

"Fine," Ms. Hannah said. But she said it in a way that meant "not fine."*

The family in front of us had six annoying kids: three boys and three girls. None of them would sit still. They were all sticking their fingers in Santa's nose, poking him in the eyes, and pulling on his beard. It took like a million hundred hours for Ms. Hannah to take a picture of each of the kids. Then she had to take a picture of just the boys. Then she had to take a picture of just the girls. Then she

---

* Only grown-ups can do that. I guess that's why we go to school—so we can learn how to say one thing and mean the exact opposite thing.

had to take a family picture. I thought I was gonna die from old age.

But finally, the last little whining nerd got up from Santa's lap. It was our turn.

"Okay, which one of you wants to go first?" asked Mrs. Roopy.

"I'm sc-scared of Santa," said Emily, who's scared of everything.

"Me too," said Alexia.

"So am I," said Andrea, Neil, Ryan, and Michael.

I had just sung that dumb rap song in front of a million hundred screaming girls. I wasn't afraid of *anything*.

"I'm not scared," I said. "I'll go first."

This was going to be the greatest moment of my life.

My Turn

10

I stepped up on the platform where Santa was sitting and climbed on his lap. Ms. Hannah told me to smile, and she snapped my picture.

This was *it*. Everything I had ever done had been leading up to this moment. Now my life was complete. If I suddenly dropped dead, at least I could say that I had met Santa Claus.

That is, if I hadn't dropped dead. Because if you're dead, you can't talk.

"Ho! Ho! Ho!" Santa said as he handed me a candy cane and a coloring book.

Whew! Santa has bad breath!

"Say, little boy, your name isn't A.J. by any chance, is it?"

"How did *you* know?" I asked.

"I'm Santa," Santa said. "I see you when you're sleeping. I know when you're awake."

"That's creepy," I said. "Do you have night vision goggles?"

"Ha! Ha! Ha!" laughed Santa. "No, but I know if you've been bad or good, A.J. Be good for goodness' sake!"

Santa must have a GPS and state-of-the-art surveillance technology. I'm not sure, but I think that's an invasion of privacy.

"So what do you want for Christmas, A.J.?" Santa asked me.

"I want the new Striker Smith

Commando," I said. "It comes with a missile launcher, voice activator, attack dog, and deluxe blowtorch. All other accessories sold separately. Batteries not included."

"Striker Smith?" said Santa. "You mean the superhero action figure from the future who travels through time and fights all who dare to thwart his destiny?"

"Yes!"

Wow, Santa really knows his toys.

"A.J., didn't I bring you a Striker Smith action figure two Christmases ago?" Santa asked me.

"Yeah," I replied. "He fell under the school bus, and his head came off."

"And didn't I bring you *another* Striker

Smith action figure last Christmas?"

"Yeah," I said. "He met his untimely end when his head got tragically melted in a battle with an evil magnifying glass."

"I'm sorry to hear that," Santa said. "I hope you'll take better care of Striker Smith *this* year."

"I will, Santa!"

"Good. Merry Christmas, A.J. Ho! Ho! Ho!"

I looked out at the kids waiting in line. I wondered how Santa would remember which presents we all asked him for.

"Are you going to write down that I asked for a Striker Smith action figure?" I asked Santa.

"That won't be necessary," he replied.

"How will you remember, Santa?"

"My mind is like a steel trap," he told me.

"You catch animals with your head?" I asked.

"No, I mean I have a good memory," Santa told me. "That's how I remember what I bring you each year."

Some of the parents in the crowd were looking at their watches. I guess my time was up. But this might be the only chance in my whole life that I would get to talk with Santa. I didn't want to leave.

"Can I ask you one question, Santa?"

"Sure, A.J."

"I understand how reindeer can fly," I said, "but doesn't your sleigh need a wing on each side, for stability?"

"The Christmas spirit lifts it up," Santa said.

"Yeah, but the sleigh doesn't look very aerodynamic," I told him. "Why not use a helicopter instead?"

"I thought you had just *one* question," Santa said.

"How is it possible to visit every house in the world in one night?" I asked. "What about the houses that don't have chimneys? What about people who live in apartments? How do you fit all the toys in the sleigh? And what do you do the rest of the year?"

"We have to wrap this up, A.J.," said Santa. "There are a lot of children waiting."

"You should really lose some weight," I told him. "Obesity is a big problem these days. Have you checked your cholesterol? Isn't it cold at the North Pole? Is there a supermarket up there? Where do you buy your groceries? Have you considered relocating to a warmer climate? Do the reindeer ever poop on people's heads?"

"Time's up, kid!" one of the parents shouted. "Let's move it along, okay?"

I got up from Santa's lap. But as I was doing that, my itchy Christmas sweater must have got caught on Santa. Because that's when the strangest thing in the history of the world happened.

His beard came off!

11

The Kid Who Ruined Christmas

"Gasp!" everyone gasped.

"Hey," I said. "You're not the *real* Santa! You're just some guy dressed *up* like Santa!"

"Uh ... well ... um ... ," Santa mumbled.

The fake Santa guy looked really familiar to me. I knew I had seen him somewhere before. So I picked his Santa hat up off his head. And you'll never believe in a million hundred years what was under there.

Nothing!

The guy was completely bald, just like Mr. Klutz, the principal of my school!

In fact, the fake Santa guy *was* Mr. Klutz!

"Mr. Klutz!" I shouted. "What are *you* doing here?"

"Uh . . . earning a little extra money over the holidays," he replied.

I knew I was in trouble as soon as people saw Santa wasn't the real Santa. But I had no idea how much trouble I was in.

"EEEEEEEK!" some girl shouted. "Santa has no hair!"

"He's a fake!" a boy yelled.

"Mommy!" screamed another girl. "You told me that man was the real Santa Claus! You lied!"

All the little kids in line started yelling, screaming, crying, and freaking out. Their parents were upset, too.

"We've been waiting in line for an *hour*," a lady shouted, "and now *this*!"

"It's *that* kid's fault!" one dad yelled,

pointing his finger at me. "He ruined Christmas for my son. He ruined Christmas for *everybody*!"

I thought I was gonna die. Mr. Klutz looked scared. He got up quickly and put a sign on his seat that said **SANTA HAS GONE TO FEED HIS REINDEER. HE'LL BE BACK SOON.**

"I'd better get out of here," he told me. "A.J., what do you have to say for yourself?"

I didn't know what to say. I didn't know what to do. I had to think fast.

"Uh, peace on earth, goodwill to men?" I said.

"Get him!" somebody shouted. "Get that kid who ruined Christmas!"

Bummer in the winter! There was only one thing I could do.

Run!

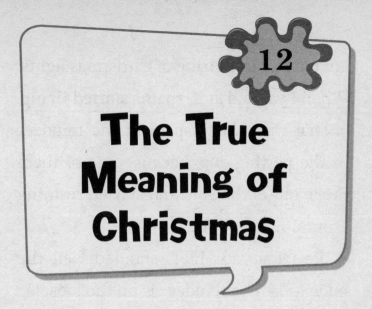

The True Meaning of Christmas

This was the worst thing to happen since TV Turnoff Week! I wanted to go to Antarctica and live with the penguins.

I jumped off the little platform to make a run for it, but I slipped on some fake snow and knocked over the Christmas tree. It landed on top of me.

As I was scrambling to get up, my foot

got tangled in a string of Christmas lights. When I yanked at it, sparks started flying.

That must have spooked the reindeer in the petting zoo, because one of them broke out of the gate and started running around in crazy circles.

"Run for your life!" shouted Neil the nude kid. "The reindeer is on the loose!"

"Watch out for those antlers!" a lady screamed.

"It's heading for the food court!" somebody shouted.

I finally got to my feet, and a bunch of angry parents started chasing me.

"Get him!" one of the dads shouted. "Get that kid!"

I bolted out of there. Crowds of people

were all over the place. I had to run around them like a football player to escape the angry parents chasing me. I bumped into some lady, and she fell into a fountain.

"Help!" I shouted. "They're gonna kill me!"

I ran up the down escalator. Then I ran down the up escalator. But I didn't travel through time. The parents were still chasing me. I couldn't lose them!

At the other end of the mall, I spotted the men's bathroom. Maybe I could hide in a stall, I figured. It was my only hope.

I ran over there and ducked inside the bathroom. I was panting and gasping for breath.

And you'll never believe who was in

there, combing his hair in the mirror.

Cray-Z!

"Dude!" he said. "What's the matter? You look like you've been through a war!"

I put my hand on his shoulder and looked him in the eye.

"You've got to help me!" I begged. "I was sitting on Santa's lap, and I accidentally pulled off his beard. The kids who were waiting in line freaked out, and now their parents are trying to get me! What should I do?"

"Quick!" Cray-Z said. "Let's switch clothes again!"

"Huh?"

"Just do it!"

I tore off my itchy Christmas sweater

and gave it to Cray-Z. He tore off his clothes and gave them to me.

"Now get out of here!" Cray-Z said. "And act casual."

I whistled as I strolled out of the bathroom.* A bunch of angry parents were milling around, looking all over. None of them noticed me. I thought I was in the clear.

But that's when the most amazing thing in the history of the world happened. An announcement came over the public address system.

Well, that's not the amazing part, because announcements come over the

---

* Because if you're whistling, nobody thinks you did anything wrong. That's the first rule of being a kid.

public address system all the time. The amazing part was what happened next.

"Attention, shoppers. It's two o'clock. The young pop sensation Cray-Z is about to do some more Christmas rapping on the main stage near the big tree. Come see him perform!"

Suddenly, Officer Spence came rolling over to me on his Segway.

"We've been looking all over for you, Mr. Z!" he said. "Come on! Everybody's waiting!"

"Huh? What? Who? Me? Again?" I asked.

Officer Spence pulled me up on the Segway and rolled over to the stage.

"Yo, Z," said the guitar player. "Let's rock, man."

There must have been a million hundred girls in the audience now. Some of them were trying to climb up on the stage, but the police were holding them back. That guy in the jacket and tie climbed up and took the microphone.

"Okay, boys and girls," he said. "Here he is again. The latest. The greatest . . . *Craaaaaaaaaaaay-Zeeeee!*"

The girls started screaming. The band started playing. I had no choice. So I started rapping. . . .

"'Twas the night before Christmas.
You know the rest.
Stuff was all over; the house was all messed.

I was dreaming of a Christmas white.
It was a totally silent night.

That's when I heard a crash and a boom,
So I ran right down to the living room.

There was this guy dressed all in black,
And over his shoulder he carried a sack.

I took one look at him and said, 'Whoa, man!
I know you're not Frosty the Snowman.'

'Who are you?' I asked after a pause.
'You sure don't look like Santa Claus.'

He said, 'The name's Klepto. I'm from
the South Pole.

I grab all your presents. That's how I roll.

'On Christmas Eve I go around the world
and steal all the presents from boys and girls.'

He went to the corner and got down on
one knee
To scoop up the gifts that were under
our tree.

He took them all. He grabbed my new toys.
He took my new clothes. He took all
our joy.

To the Christmas Klepto, everything's free.
'I'll take your partridge,' he said, 'and
your pear tree.

'I like your presents, and now they're
mine.
Say, how much of this stuff did you buy
online?

'You better watch out. You better not cry.
You make one peep, and I'll poke out
your eye.'

'You're a mean man, sir!' I said with a hiss.
Just wait until Santa finds out about this.'

That Mr. Klepto thought he was a smarty,
But in the end, we spoiled his party.

Oh sure, the guy had lots of charm,
Until he tripped our silent alarm.

A few minutes later, the cops arrived.
Mr. Klepto, under the couch he dived.

The cops yelled, 'Come out with your
hands in the air.'
'I was framed!' he shouted. 'This ain't
fair!'

The cops said, 'Now don't try anything
violent.
All you have is the right to remain silent.'

They dragged him away, and he said,
'Bye-bye.'
And that was the last I heard of that
guy.

Now all this stuff that I've been rappin'
You may say that none of it happened.

After all, nobody came and stole your stuff.
Nobody broke in. Nobody got rough.

Well, the reason that you've got nothing to fear
Is because they put Klepto away for ten years!

So you can believe what you want to believe,
But that's what happened on Christmas Eve."

"Let's hear it for Cray-Z!" said the guy with the jacket and tie.

The girls went nuts, screaming and yelling and freaking out. I jumped off the stage and ran back to the men's room. Cray-Z was in there waiting for me.

"You saved my life," I told him.

"Now we're even, dude."

Cray-Z and I switched back into our normal clothes, shook hands, and said good-bye. As I was about to walk away, I came up with the greatest idea in the history of the world.

"Hey, Cray-Z. I need to get a Christmas present for my sister. Can you give me an autograph?"

"Sure, dude," he said.

Cray-Z took off his hat. He pulled a Sharpie from his pocket, signed the hat, and handed it to me.

"Y'know," he said, "sometimes I wish I was in your shoes."

"Why?" I asked. "What's wrong with *your* shoes?"

"No," he said, "what I mean is that the grass is always greener on the other side."

"Huh?" I asked. "What does the color of grass have to do with anything?"

That Cray-Z kid is weird. Who cares about shoes and grass?

But as I walked away, I started thinking about what Cray-Z said. Christmas isn't about malls and elves and trees and presents. It's about being a good person. It's about helping a guy out when he's in trouble. Cray-Z needed my help, so I helped him. Then I needed *his* help, and he helped me. Christmas is a time for giving. *That's* the true meaning of Christmas spirit.

Who knows? Maybe I'll become Cray-Z's stunt double. Maybe Santa will bring me the new Striker Smith Commando action figure with missile launcher, voice activator, attack dog, and deluxe blowtorch. Maybe another song will get stuck in my head. Maybe the real Santa will come to the mall next Christmas.

Maybe they'll pay the teachers more money so they don't have to dress up like elves. Maybe I'll travel back in time on an escalator. Maybe Santa will get some breath mints. Maybe I won't have to wear my itchy Christmas sweater next year. Maybe I'll get to eat some of those giant nuts. Maybe Santa will be arrested for invading people's privacy. Maybe Mr. Klutz will catch animals with his head. Maybe Santa will ditch his sleigh and switch to a helicopter. Maybe Andrea and Emily will bring peace and harmony to kids all over the world.

But it won't be easy!

MY
WeiRd
SchooL
SpeciaL

Deck the Halls, We're Off the Walls!

Weird Extras!

★ Professor A.J.'s Weird Christmas Facts

★ Fun Games and Weird-Word Puzzles

★ My Weird School Trivia Questions

PROFESSOR A. J.'S WEIRD CHRISTMAS FACTS

Howdy, My Weird School fans! Professor A.J. here. I'm gonna tell you a bunch of stuff you probably don't know about Christmas. It's really important for you to learn stuff so you won't grow up to be a dumbhead like a certain person in my class with curly brown hair who rolls her eyes and says mean things to me all the time. But it wouldn't be polite to name names.*

First of all, do you know how the tradition of the Christmas tree got started? It was

* Andrea

back in 1897. On Christmas Eve that year, a huge pine tree fell on top of a house in Lake Placid, New York. The Bates family was just sitting down to their Christmas dinner when the tree crashed through their roof and landed in their living room. The family freaked out and were really angry that they would have to spend their Christmas Eve getting that dumb tree out of their living room. So they decided just to leave it there. And ever since that day, people have been putting trees in their living rooms at Christmastime.

Okay, I totally made that story up, so nah-nah-nah boo-boo on you!

But here's some *true* stuff about Christmas. . . .

FACT:

—The first song to be broadcast from space was "Jingle Bells", on December 16, 1965. The crew of the *Gemini 6* sang the song and played a harmonica.

Most people don't know that the astronauts *wanted* to play the song on a piano, but it wouldn't fit in the space capsule.

FACT:
—Do you know what the word "mistletoe" really means? You better sit down for this one. **Mistletoe means "dung on a twig."**

That's right! Bird dung! Honest, I did not make that up. You can't make up stuff that good.

FACT:

—You know that character **Tiny Tim** in Charles Dickens's classic *A Christmas Carol*? Well, before he named the character Tiny Tim, Dickens considered naming the character **Puny Pete, Small Sam,** or **Little Larry.**

Ha! I bet that book would have sold a lot more copies if he titled it *Puny Pete Has Nothing to Eat!*

FACT:

—In Columbus, Texas, they have a Santa Claus Museum. There are more than two thousand Santas on display.

The museum even has a Santa doorbell!

FACT:

—Foreign languages are weird. If you wanted to say "Merry Christmas" in Italian, you'd say "*Buon Natale.*" In Spanish it's "*Feliz Navidad.*" In French it's "*Joyeux Noël.*" In German it's "*Frohe Weihnachten.*"

And if you were in outer space and you said "Merry Christmas" to somebody, you would die instantly, because there's no oxygen in outer space.

FACT:

—In Italy they celebrate Christmas on January 6. They call it the Feast of the Epiphany. A witch called La Befana rides on her broomstick the night before and fills kids' stockings with presents if they're good and lumps of coal if they're bad.

That's why I'll never go to Italy over Christmas vacation. First of all, boys have to wear stockings. Not only that, but you might have to walk around in stockings with coal in them. That would hurt!

—Speaking of stockings, kids once used their regular old socks for presents from Santa. That came from an old Dutch tradition in which kids would leave their shoes out with food for Saint Nicholas's donkeys, and he would leave presents in return.

Ugh, disgusting! Dutch people put food in their shoes and let donkeys eat out of them. They're weird.

FACT:
—Did you know that the United States has an official Christmas tree? It's a giant sequoia in California that's over 1,500 years old.

Wow, that's almost as old as my parents.

I could tell you a lot more stuff about Christmas, but I'd rather open my presents and go play out in the snow. Happy holidays!

Professor A.J. (the professor of awesomeness)

FUN GAMES AND WEIRD-WORD PUZZLES

I. WHERE'S SANTA?

Directions: Santa needs to deliver his gifts, but he doesn't want to be seen! Can you find where he is hidden in this picture?

2. WINTER WORD JUMBLE

Directions: The eight words below are all jumbled up! Can you put the letters in correct order and uncover the holiday words?

1. PNSRETE: _____

2. YJO: _____

3. WOSMNAN: _____

4. SBLLE: _____

5. EGIHLS: _____

6. SCHNETTSU: _____

7. CNRAUERTKC: _____

8. DRNEIREE: _____

3. GIFT GIVER

Directions: Everyone has something special they want for Christmas. Match these weird people and animals below with the gift that they would most want from Santa!

4. SNOWFLAKE MATCH

Directions: Snowflakes are falling! Each snowflake is an identical match with another snowflake on the page. Can you find all the matches?

5. CRAZY-CHRISTMAS WORD SEARCH

Directions: Can you find all ten Christmas words that are hidden in this messy jumble of letters?

```
E K A L F W O N S E F U V S M
M O E Z V L X Q I V L D X I W
Q X C L H X D Y W L D F S K M
U M A F O Q S X W F O T X I P
C D N G H P E W J F L W T H X
R W D K C L H K X E D A P T I
K Y Y I X H Z T T M R K A S U
B C C A X J R O R E D C G T X
X V A H J F E I T O G G C N R
B L N B H X B N S W N B I E Y
B C E N T U I W Q T H N S S G
I F Q Y H W O F J L M R B E M
J I N G L E B E L L S A M R V
A N G E L D W W P Q M W S P A
Y S U N Z M F I P S R X K A P
```

ANGEL CHRISTMAS ELF JINGLE BELLS
MISTLETOE CANDY CANE NORTH POLE
PRESENTS SNOWFLAKE WINTER

6. ORNAMENT OOPS

Directions: The ornaments on this Christmas tree all spell special holiday words, but it seems that a few have gone missing! Can you figure out the missing letters in each of these words? After you've found all of the letters, put them in order on the lines below the tree to reveal the answer to the mystery question!

_ _ E R _ Y

_ _ T O _ K I N G

H O _ I D _ Y

S _ G A R P L U M _

Who Is Santa's Favorite Helper?

_ _ _ . _ _ _ _ _

MY WEIRD SCHOOL
TRIVIA QUESTIONS

There's no way in a million hundred years you'll get all these answers right. So nah-nah-nah boo-boo on you!

Q: WHAT IS A.J.'S SISTER'S NAME?
A: Amy

Q: WHICH STAFF MEMBER INVENTED A SECRET LANGUAGE THAT MAKES NO SENSE?
A: Mrs. Kormel

Q: WHAT IS MS. HANNAH'S DRESS MADE OF?
A: Pot holders she bought on eBay

Q: WHERE DO THE KIDS EAT LUNCH?
A: In the vomitorium

Q: HOW DID MISS SMALL BREAK HER LEG?
A: She fell out of a tree.

Q: WHAT DOES ANDREA DO EVERY THURSDAY AFTER SCHOOL?
A: Clog dancing

Q: WHAT IS ANDREA'S FAVORITE MOVIE?
A: Annie

Q: WHO DOES A.J. WANT TO MARRY WHEN HE GROWS UP?
A: Mrs. Cooney, the nurse

Q: WHAT DOES YAWYE STAND FOR?
A: You Are What You Eat

Q: WHO IS ELLA MENTRY SCHOOL NAMED AFTER?

A: Ella Mentry

Q: WHAT DOES MISS LAZAR HAVE IN HER SECRET ROOM DOWN IN THE BASEMENT?

A: A museum of toilet-bowl plungers

Q: WHY DOESN'T A.J. HAVE AN INVISIBLE FRIEND ANYMORE?

A: He got into an argument with his invisible friend, so they stopped being friends.

Q: WHAT FUEL POWERS MR. DOCKER'S CAR?

A: Potatoes

Q: WHAT IS BRAINWASHING?

A: That's when bald guys shampoo their head

Q: WHAT IS A.J.'S FAVORITE HOLIDAY?

A: Take Our Daughters to Work Day, because Andrea is absent from school

Q: WHY IS PRESIDENT'S DAY SPECIAL, ACCORDING TO MICHAEL?

A: Because that's the day big-screen TVs go on sale

Q: WHY ARE SHOVELS BETTER THAN COMPUTERS?

A: Because you can't dig a hole with a computer

Q: WHAT DOES IT MEAN WHEN TEACHERS MAKE A PEACE SIGN WITH THEIR FINGERS?

A: It means "shut up."

Q: WHY DO YOU CLAP AT THE END OF AN ASSEMBLY?

A: Because you're glad it's over

Q: HOW DOES MRS. YONKERS POWER HER COMPUTER?

A: She runs on a giant hamster wheel.

Q: WHAT IS SPECIAL ABOUT MRS. YONKERS'S PENCIL SHARPENER?

A: It is remote-controlled.

Q: WHAT IS DR. CARBLES'S FIRST NAME?

A: He wants to be Frank, but his name is Milton.

Q: WHERE DOES MR. KLUTZ GET A PIG?

A: From Rent-A-Pig

ANSWER KEY

WHERE'S SANTA?

WINTER WORD JUMBLE

1. PNSRETE: PRESENT
2. YJO: JOY
3. WOSMNAN: SNOWMAN
4. SBLLE: BELLS
5. EGIHLS: SLEIGH
6. SCHNETTSU: CHESTNUTS
7. CNRAUERTKC: NUTCRACKER
8. DRNEIREE: REINDEER

GIFT GIVER

SNOWFLAKE MATCH

CRAZY-CHRISTMAS WORD SEARCH

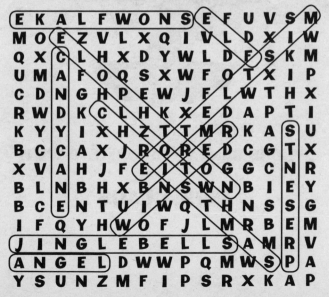

ORNAMENT OOPS

WHO IS SANTA'S FAVORITE HELPER?

MRS. CLAUS

THE LAST OF THE MOHICANS

NOTES

including
- *General Plot Summary*
- *List of Characters*
- *Summaries and Commentaries*
- *Critical Analysis*
- *Glossary*
- *Questions for Review*

by
Thomas J. Rountree, Ph.D.
University of Alabama

Wiley Publishing, Inc.

About the Author
Thomas J. Rountree, Ph.D.
University of Alabama

Production
Wiley Indianapolis Composition Services

CliffsNotes™ *The Last of the Mohicans*

Published by:
Wiley Publishing, Inc.
909 Third Avenue
New York, NY 10022
www.wiley.com

CONTENTS

THE LAST OF THE MOHICANS

INTRODUCTION

The year 1826 was momentous for James Cooper—then and afterwards. Since his birth in 1789, he had been nurtured on frontier life in New York State until 1803, expelled from Yale for his pranks in 1805, sent to sea as a common sailor in 1806, warranted a midshipman from 1808 until 1810 when he retired after the political assassination of his father, married in 1811, and made head of the entire Cooper clan in 1819 when the last of his five elder brothers died. Between that time and 1826 he had published five novels (the first one on a dare), becoming America's first significant novelist and setting the tone and the scene for many other American novels, including some of his own, that were yet to come: the temporal and geographical locales of colonial and revolutionary America, the frontier, and the sea.

Then in 1826 he made three departures. He added *Fenimore* to his name and he sailed for what became a seven-year sojourn in Europe. But more important for American letters, instead of moving immediately to new literary subject matter, he turned again to the subject that was to be his most enduring one and was to occupy his creative thought off and on until 1841—the tragic subject of the frontier and the noble but necessarily expendable frontiersman, Natty Bumppo. The novel of that year was *The Last of the Mohicans,* the second of five books to focus on the expanding fringe of American civilization and the stalwart white nomad who helped make that expansion and his own subsequent demise a mythic reality. And of all the thirty-odd novels that Cooper was to complete, it was *The Last of the Mohicans* that was to become his "classic" in both fact and spirit.

Today's reader, geared to a modern tempo and coming again or coming fresh upon Cooper's work, may wonder what all the acclaim was and is about. For Cooper was a popular and financial success here in America, while his acknowledged eminence abroad led, long before his death, to translations in all the languages of Western Europe, plus those of Persia, Egypt, and Turkey. Hence, like Dickens' later, Cooper's work was often as popular overseas as at home. In 1828, for instance, the composer Franz Schubert, lying near death in Vienna, asked a friend to rush him Cooper's latest book in print; and nearly a century later when in 1917 the United

States entered World War I on the side of France, a Frenchman toasted his surprised American listeners by calling out, "The spirit of Leather-Stocking is awake!" Thus among the nicknames for Natty Bumppo (Deer-slayer, Hawkeye, Pathfinder, Leather-Stocking, the trapper), Leather-Stocking became the common one attached to the character and to the series of five novels. In *The Last of the Mohicans* Natty is called Hawkeye, and it is the acclaim for and value of this novel and character that the present summaries and commentaries are planned to clarify — as a guide to, and not a substitute for, the work itself. The wise student will want the full meal rather than a capsule of vitamins only, and he will place his emphasis where it belongs — on the actual novel.

To appreciate the novel properly, the modern reader needs to remember something of the method of publication in Cooper's day. Like his other novels, *The Last of the Mohicans* was published in two volumes, a predetermined circumstance that partly accounts for the major division of the novel into two long chase sequences with a short intermediate stay of relative safety for the main characters at Fort William Henry. Herein is the big pattern of the book, based upon the suspenseful technique that Cooper made famous in novel after novel: pursuit-capture-escape-and-pursuit. The demands of publication, then, as well as the nature of his subject matter and his own propensities as a writer, are operative in this classic of patterned adventure.

Similarly, publishers' deadlines, readers with the leisure and desire for long contact with fictional characters and situations, the rapid writing pace that Cooper set himself, and his honesty in doing what he did best — all were instrumental in evolving the amazing improvisation in this and other novels by Cooper. Here he stays within the confines of frontier adventure and within the form and structure of the novel. But in his professional field, Cooper is as inventive as twentieth-century jazz and modern ballet; and the present-day reader should need only to shift his tolerance from one subject and form to another in order to appreciate — and probably enjoy — this early American classic that explores one of our greatest traditions and first bodies forth at its best what is doubtless *the* American myth.

That tradition is the idea of the frontier, as old as the discovery of the New World and as young as recent national governmental slogans and the Peace Corps. In *The Last of the Mohicans* the frontier is both a place and a condition made up of opposite, usually conflicting forces, for the very nature of a frontier is that it is the demarcating area where things come together with all their differences. In the pervading historical background of the novel is the conflict between civilization and so-called savagism: the wresting of a continent from nature and the Indians. More immediate is the clash between the French and the English for colonial control of the land (the time of the novel, we remember, is the summer of 1757); and for mercenary help these two nationalities make impermanent, weathercock alliances with already hostile Indians whom Cooper presents as the bad Iroquois stock and the good Delawares and Mohicans of Algonquin stock. The historical confrontation of races is brought into fictional focus with the skirmishes and occasional understandings between individuals and groups of reds and whites, both of whom are in turn at odds with peoples of their own color. One symbolic result is the death of the last offspring of the admirable Mohicans. But what T. S. Eliot would call the "objective correlative" of this problem is also presented dramatically in terms of miscegenation: the tragic mutual love of the noble Indian Uncas and the sentimentalized yet nonetheless worthy Cora Munro, who is also desired by the red villain Magua. In the novel this thematic problem is slow in development—we are, in fact, hardly aware of it until mid-point—and even as it comes into the forefront of action toward the end, it is muted by Cooper at the very time that it becomes the most immediate motivation for the hair-raising events that bring the novel to its close. Without doubt, the novel throughout is one of the bloodiest in American literature, and that tragic bloodshed stems from the fact that, in general historic background and dramatic fictional foreground, human beings are involved in a concept of progress that irresistibly pushes the frontier westward.

Cooper can encompass this situation convincingly because it is history extending into his own lifetime: during the 1820's and 1830's the United States policy of Removal was steadily shifting the Indians to areas west of the Mississippi River. But he can convince us also because of a natural paradox in himself. As a son of eighteenth-century rationalism (especially Scottish) he believed that everything had its "place," a belief that stratified society and even government. It was this conviction that led him through his spokesman Hawkeye to insist upon the rightness of Indian "gifts" and white "gifts" and upon the impropriety even after death of a union between Uncas and Cora. At the same time Cooper was heir to the idea of progress which in America became a "manifest destiny" to press civilization all the way to the Pacific Ocean. When the force of progress confronted the condition of "place," the latter too often gave at its foundations and the result was tragic turmoil that simply used and sometimes obliterated the tribes of "savage" Indians, that foreordained the fatality of love crossing the racial line, that called for the expendability of a Natty Bumppo who could be what he could only be, a frontiersman, as long as the frontier was stationary and consistent unto itself. It is this tragic meeting of differences comprising the idea of the frontier that gives power to Cooper's novel, even as he attempts to entertain his nineteenth-century reader with the elements of improvised adventure and of current sentimental love novels.

In the middle of these differing forces is Hawkeye, the first great fictional embodiment of the American myth. Based on real-life prototypes but with only a vague resemblance to Daniel Boone, Hawkeye is the frontiersman par excellence and the literary forefather of every fictional cowboy and his sort who since then has climbed from or onto his horse, prepared to defend the good with his deadly, unerring bullets and the strength of his endurance. Compared with him, the finest Indians like the last two Mohicans are a close second best, while a white like Major Heyward, though top-rate within the discipline of his own civilized milieu, is third-rate in coping with the uncertainties of frontier existence. The reason is that, while none of these were strictly born of the frontier, Hawkeye was. In growing up and living there, he has retained the morals of his civilized inheritance and acquired only the virtues and woodsmanship of the Indians. Thus he is not a full member of either side in the conflict. Instead, he is a quiet, unassuming, even background figure of the highest ideals who serves as mediator and who is made believably human because of minor frailties like his boasting pride in marksmanship. Although his is a life-long brotherly attachment to Chingachgook, he is essentially and sadly (but rightly if he is to remain true to his nature) alone, monolithic and ideally enduring at the same time that he must ultimately vanish with the geographical frontier. Acquaintance with the entire Leather-Stocking series gives one the fullest awareness of the stature and meaning of Hawkeye, but both qualities are apparent in *The Last of the Mohicans* through Hawkeye's singular uprightness, his wide renown across the plains and forests, and his rather aloof involvement in the actions of the story. It is, in fact, his combination of ideals and aloofness that fits him to be Cooper's commentator on the beauties and perversities of nature and human life. He is too good to be an actuality, but he is as living as any just ideal can be, even after he and his frontier have vanished. Thus, to a great extent due to Cooper, the idea of a Natty Bumppo remains, carrying with it that hazy degree of reality, truth, and effectiveness that is the province of myth.

The novel, never meant to be realistic in any strict sense, is of course filled out with a profusion of other conventions and motifs. Cooper's appreciation for primeval nature is obvious in the choice of modulated phrasing and in the descriptive accuracy of his scenes. When he goes into detail about tracking fugitives through the forests, he is both recognizing and fulfilling the typical American interest in know-how. Features of the sentimental novel with its excessively emotional view of experience abound. And though it is sporadic and sometimes heavy-handed, humor too is not lacking, for the traditional comic Yankee character finds a role here in David Gamut. But all of these elements and others in the novel are subsumed by the dominant serious theme. For the story of *The Last of the Mohicans,* the episodic adventures are the appropriate fictional clothing, while the conventional sentimental love represents the alluring piping. The vibrant thematic life underneath all this, with an ultimately doomed Hawkeye at the center, is the condition of the frontier with its heroics, its bloodshed, and its tragedy.

GENERAL PLOT SUMMARY

Guided by the displaced Huron warrior Magua, four people — Major Duncan Heyward, Psalmodist David Gamut, and Alice and Cora Munro — strike through the wilderness forest for Fort William Henry, which is besieged by the French near Lake George. Led astray by Magua, they encounter the white woodsman Hawkeye and his two Mohican companions, Chingachgook and Uncas, whereupon the villainous Huron escapes.

Traveling to the safety of the caves at Glenn's Falls, the party is attacked by Indians early the next morning. Running out of munitions, the three woodsmen escape downriver for help, but the others are captured and taken away by a splinter group of warriors headed by Magua. After a long journey, the Huron coldly proposes to Cora, whose refusal brings an attack upon the captives, who are saved by the sudden arrival of the three woodsmen. All the Indians are killed except Magua, who gets away again.

Leading the party of protagonists through narrow escapes from Indians and then besieging Frenchmen, Hawkeye brings them to a mountainside vantage point overlooking the fort. During the trip a quiet interest develops between the young Uncas and the brunette Cora, while Heyward shows a deference toward Alice. With difficulty finding their way through the heavy morning mists and the omnipresent French, the seven, hotly pursued, finally reach the fort, where Commander Munro recognizes the voice of his daughter Alice and opens a sally-port for them. Therewith Heyward leads a repulse of the pursuing Frenchmen.

With the passage of days, a parley is held and, since General Webb is sending no help, Munro agrees to surrender. Meanwhile Heyward learns that Cora's darkened aspect lies not only in a brooding nature but also in the fact that she is part Negro. During the planned withdrawal of the English forces, the Indians begin a bloody massacre and Magua once again escapes with the two girls and Gamut.

Three days later the three woodsmen, Munro, and Heyward go north of the lake and across the country in pursuit. When Uncas is captured by the Hurons, Hawkeye effects his escape and Alice's through disguise and all head for the Delaware village where Cora is held captive. Magua follows and demands his prisoners. Uncas reveals himself as a chief to the patriarch Tamenund, and Magua is allowed his only rightful prisoner, Cora, though the protagonists and the Delawares vow to follow and regain her freedom. Coming out of hiding in a beaver pond, Chingachgook and Munro join the ensuing battle in which the Hurons are defeated. Nonetheless Magua and two warriors escape with Cora through the nearby caves and up a mountainside. Finally cornered by Hawkeye, Heyward, Gamut, and Uncas, the Hurons give defiance and in the fighting Cora, Uncas, and Magua are killed.

The next day is one of mourning for the Delawares. Cora and Uncas are buried side by side, and all the white characters except Hawkeye leave. When Chingachgook states that he is now alone, Hawkeye grasps his hand and declares that such is not so. At the same time Tamenund sadly comments upon the worsening historic plight of the American Indians and particularly upon the tragically accomplished demise of the wise and noble race of Mohicans.

CHARACTERS

Chingachgook
Known also as Le Gros Serpent, he is the noble Mohican woodsman who has been the life-long friend of Hawkeye.

Uncas
The son of Chingachgook, he is the last of the Mohicans. Popularly called Le Cerf Agile, he is a significant participant in one of the two love stories in the novel, and his tragic death marks the death of the entire tribe of Mohicans.

David Gamut
Follows the profession of the psalmodist, carrying his faith through song into the wilderness. He functions as a comic persona and as a partially developing character reacting to conditions of the frontier.

Hawkeye
His real name is Natty Bumppo and his wide reputation as a rifle-man has given him the additional moniker of La Longue Carabine. He is technically the main protagonist because of his abiding position in the total plot and because of his pervading image as the upright, ideal individual-ist who has taken unto himself the best of both civilization and so-called savagery.

Major Duncan Heyward
The sentimental hero in the second love story. Though a brave and active man, as a characterization he is limited to unoriginality because he comes straight from the stereotyped tradition of the sentimental novel. He often serves merely as a foil to the knowledgeable frontiersmen.

Magua
Accurately nicknamed Le Renard Subtil, he is the antagonist, a dis-possessed and displaced Huron and a thorough villain, though his complex motivations make him a convincingly well rounded fictional character.

General Montcalm
Marquis Louis Joseph de Saint-Veran, is the opposing French mili-tarist who captures Fort William Henry and whose laxity allows the infamous Indian massacre.

Colonel Munro
He commands Fort William Henry until its fall, after which he goes into a steady decline. He is the father of Alice and Cora, whose determina-tion to visit him during crisis instigates the action of the novel.

Alice Munro
The sentimental love heroine who complements Major Hey-ward, is palely flower-like and lacks real vitality.

Cora Munro
The darker and older sister, is involved in the tragedy of miscegena-tion. A far more convincing characterization than Alice, she is beloved of the admirable Indian Uncas.

Tamenund
He appears late in the novel as the venerable patriarch of the Delaware Indians. Because of his experience and length of life (he has survived three gen-erations of warriors) he is revered as judge, decision-maker, and spokesman.

12

General Webb

He appears in the early scene so briefly that the reader forgets ever seeing him, and has background importance as the officer who declines to send adequate support to the besieged Fort William Henry.

(Note: Numerous minor characters, such as the cowardly young Huron and his father, appear with brief significance to plot or theme, but they seldom are named.)

SUMMARIES AND COMMENTARIES

COOPER'S THREE PREFACES

Summary

Cooper's preface to the 1826 edition is a kind of defense, stressing that the novel is "a narrative" with historical allusions, of which the Indian history calls for some comment. He racially and geographically places the Mohicans as a disappearing tribe of the Wapanachki or Lenni Lenape stock (known today as the Algonquin) who were bounded by the Penobscot and the Potomac, the Atlantic and the Mississippi. To the north were the Mengwe (or Iroquois) stock and their confederacy of Six Nations (that is, six major tribes); they were contemptuously called "Mingoes" by the Lenape. Cooper concludes by whimsically warning young ladies, bachelors, and clergymen from reading his "shocking" book.

The 1831 introduction (reprinted in 1850 with two paragraphs deleted and a new one added) repeats some of the earlier preface but discusses the Asiatic origin of the Indian and his two opposing attitudes in war and peace. Cooper points to the importance of the scout Hawkeye as a "fanciful" character whose purpose "is poetically to furnish a witness to the truth of...the progress of the American nation."

The 1850 preface to the Leather-Stocking Tales discusses the chronology of the five novels and their preeminence among Cooper's works. Leather-Stocking is the kind of "beau-ideal" character allowable in the fiction of romances. While his "great rules of conduct" come from the best in civilized and savage life and are natural to him and his situation, "in a moral sense this man of the forest is purely a creation."

Commentary

These prefaces show the growth of Cooper's reflections about the novel from the specific to the general as he gets a more critical grasp on what he has in part intuitively created. His defensive explanations shift from historic details to comments on the ideal in fiction. In all instances the intention is to clarify and justify what follows.

CHAPTERS 1 AND 2

Summary

Before any characters appear, the time and geography are made clear. Though it is the last war that England and France waged for a country that neither would retain, the wilderness between the forces still always has to be overcome first. Thus it is in 1757 in the New York area between the head waters of the Hudson River and Lake George (the "Horican") to the north. Because only two years earlier General Braddock was disgracefully routed by a handful of French and Indians, the frontier is now exposed to real and imaginary savage disasters as well as to the horrors of warfare. Fear has replaced reason.

Near dusk of a day in July an Indian runner named Magua arrives at Fort Edward on the upper Hudson. He has come from Fort William Henry at the southern tip of Lake George with the news that the French General Montcalm is moving south with a very large army and that Munro, commander of Fort William Henry, is in urgent need of plentiful reinforcements from General Webb. Early the next morning a limited detachment of fifteen hundred regulars and colonists departs as if swallowed by the forest.

Shortly afterwards Major Duncan Heyward and Alice and Cora Munro, guided by Magua on foot, take by horseback a secret route toward William Henry for the girls to join their father. Blonde Alice is doubtful about Magua, covered with war paint and showing a sullen fierceness; but dark-haired Cora is stoically common sense about him, even though Heyward mentions that their father had once had to deal rigidly with the Indian. As the small party pushes on. they are overtaken by David Gamut, a tall, ungainly psalmodist (singing-master) ridiculously dressed and carrying a pitch pipe while riding a mare followed by its young colt. He desires to join them, and after some banter between him and Alice, he pulls out the twenty-sixth edition of *The Bay Psalm Book,* sounds his pipe, and renders a song "in full, sweet, and melodious tones." At a muttered comment from Magua, Heyward insists upon silence for safety. Then he glances about them and, satisfied that he has seen only shining berries, smiles to himself as they move on. But he is wrong. The branches move and a wild savage peers exultingly after them as they disappear among the dark lines of trees.

Commentary

These two chapters introduce the reader to the historical and natural settings and are indicative of the extent to which this book, as a historical novel, relates its fictional characters to real history. Only here at the beginning and later at mid-novel will the action coincide in detail with actual events, though the historic war is always somewhere in the near distance. These chapters also present four of the main fictional characters and one secondary one, all of whom will merit our concern henceforth. Major Heyward is the gallant romantic hero; but unlike most sentimental romances where for each hero there is one heroine, here there are two, Alice and Cora, blonde and brunette. And it is immediately apparent that the old tradition of weak-blonde-strong-brunette contrast is at work, stereotyping the fair Alice and dark Cora. These three are rather predictable types which both simplify and stultify the writer's efforts with them. Magua's stealthy eyes and abrupt, furtive actions mark him as a potential villain, while the exaggerated presentation of the simple, single-minded Gamut paints him as the comic and perhaps pitiable adult innocent. At this point both are something less than realistic and fully vitalized characters, but in comparison to the other three they seem to breathe real air. The stature of originality and verisimilitude that they do show is doubtless due to the fact that they are native characters. One may note, for instance, that Heyward's comment about Munro's once dealing rigidly with Magua not only lends suspense to the situation and points to the theme of revenge but also suggests some depth of motivation for the Indian.

What we call plot — the complications of a situation and the subsequent events and actions that further entangle things before they are finally resolved in some fashion — starts an early ferment in terms of danger and suspense. Four likable and somewhat innocent characters strike into the unknown forest wilderness with a doubtful savage guide. It is a time of urgency, and movement is swift. Cooper hardly gives the reader time to question seriously why Munro's daughters would push forward their visit at this worst of times and would feel themselves safer almost alone on a dim path in savage-infested territory than in the company of fifteen hundred trained fighting men. This represents a lack in character motivation, but Cooper knows that he must get his people into jeopardy, and he at least partly succeeds in hiding this lack under suspenseful action and a sense of urgency. But in spite of the pace, Cooper also manages a good instance of dramatic irony, a fictional presentation in which the reader is allowed to see or deduce predicaments unknown or only partly known by the characters. It is thus that the first part of the pattern of action — that of pursuit — has begun.

CHAPTER 3

Summary

In another part of the forest by the river a few miles to the west, Hawkeye and Chingachgook appear to be waiting for someone as they talk with low voices. It is now afternoon. The Indian and the scout are attired according to their forest habits: Chingachgook with his semi-nude, war-painted body and scalping tuft of hair, his tomahawk, scalping knife, and short rifle; Hawkeye with his hunting shirt, skin cap, buckskin leggings, knife, pouch and horn, and long rifle. They discuss their respective forefathers, and Chingachgook relates the slow demise of his tribe of Mohicans so that only he and his son Uncas now remain. At the mention of his name Uncas, a youthful warrior dressed much like Hawkeye, appears and says that he has been on the trail of the Maquas, another name for the Mengwe or Iroquois, their natural enemies. The antlers of a deer are seen in the distance, and Hawkeye is about to shoot the animal for food when the warrior warns him that a shot will warn the enemy. Just as Uncas kills it with an arrow, they hear the sounds of feet which Chingachgook recognizes as the horses of white men.

Commentary

This chapter introduces the other three main actors in the story. Through the talk of the scout and the senior Indian, the rightness of racial "gifts" is established. Their discussion of differences between currents and tides, between the large salt ocean and the smaller fresh lakes, reflects the novel's central stable motif of relativity as Hawkeye concludes that "everything depends on what scale you look at things." Hawkeye's precipitant movement to shoot the deer at first makes his awareness of the forest dangers questionable; but the need for action is natural to this kind of man after idleness, and the incident shows his pride in handling his rifle. Such an incident makes this ideal frontiersman also human. By the end of this chapter all the principal characters are introduced, with each one's general qualities established. They are about to be brought together to participate in the first long chase sequence.

CHAPTER 4

Summary

When the mounted party from Fort Howard approaches the three men of the woods, Hawkeye addresses first Gamut and then Heyward only to learn that they are lost because their Indian guide has taken them west instead of north toward Fort William Henry. Doubtful, especially when he learns that the guide is a Huron who has been adopted by the Mohawks,

Hawkeye makes an *a priori* judgment of the still unseen guide and uses the contemptuous term *Mingo:* "he who is born a Mingo will die a Mingo." Ejaculations from his two Indian companions indicate that they concur with his thinking.

Still doubting and cautious, he baits Heyward by bantering away about Indians until Heyward reveals that he is the major of the 60th regiment of the king at William Henry. Walking to the rear of the party for a look at Magua, Hawkeye returns and says that he could guide them back to Fort Edward, which is only an hour's journey away, but that it would be impossible because of the ladies and the dangers of coming night, particularly with the Mohawk as a companion. He suggests his shooting and disabling Magua from where he stands, but the major will not hear of it. Consequently, as the sun goes down, he sends the two Mohicans through the thickets on opposite sides of the path and tells the major to engage Magua in talk while he himself converses with Gamut.

Magua proudly refers to himself as Le Renard Subtil (the Subtle Fox), the name his Canada fathers have given him. He is cautiously quiet but allows Heyward to convince him to sit and eat. As slight sounds in the thicket make Le Renard alert, Heyward dismounts, determined to seize the treacherous guide. But the latter strikes up the major's arm, gives a piercing cry, and darts away into the thicket. Immediately Chingachgook and Uncas appear and give swift pursuit just as a flash comes from Hawkeye's rifle.

Commentary

Since this chapter is mostly one of surface action, little comment is needed except to point out Hawkeye's respect for the military and the fact that all Iroquois tribes are to be looked upon as treacherous enemies. The alertness and swift action of Magua, who is more of a threat when they do not know his whereabouts, mark him as a worthy opponent for the stalwart protagonists. His escape heightens the suspense of the story.

CHAPTER 5

Summary

The pursuit of Magua is unsuccessful, but Hawkeye feels that he has wounded him slightly and is certain of it when they find bloodstains on the sumach leaves. Heyward wants to continue the chase, but the scout fears an ambush, particularly since he has fired his rifle, an action for which he upbraids himself. With night almost upon them, the three woodsmen confer and, at the urging of Uncas, decide to take the group to their "harboring place" after Heyward promises to keep the place a secret.

The horses are a problem, but rather than give them their bridles, the men agree to mislead the foe into thinking that the group is on horseback. When the colt makes a noise in the bush, the scout determines that of necessity it must die so that it cannot betray them. Uncas shoots it with an arrow and Chingachgook quickly and mercifully slits its throat and dashes it into the river to float away. While the Indians lead the horses into the river, Hawkeye and Heyward place the females in a bark canoe and, trailed by the dejected Gamut, wade in to bear it upstream toward the waterfall, passing the dark overhang of the bank where the horses are now hidden.

At the falls the scout seats all the whites in the canoe and poles it into the center of the turbulent stream where it is whirled about until he brings it to rest beside a flat rock. "You are at the foot of Glenn's," he says and takes the canoe to fetch the Mohicans and the venison. When they are all together, he worriedly tells that the horses had cowered as if they scented wolves that would hover near Indian kills. He is interrupted by a sad song from Gamut, whom he tries to console for the death of the colt. Then he and the two Mohicans disappear in succession, "seeming to vanish against the dark face of a perpendicular rock."

Commentary

Here the reader encounters the first bloodshed born of war. The wounding of Magua and the killing of the innocent colt stand in contrast to the preceding shooting of the deer for food. Now that the two parties have become one by virtue of survival necessities, Hawkeye shows his skill as a woodsman who also knows his enemies' ways. He stands forth as a decisive character.

Gamut too grows in characterization. While the two girls give simple female reactions to the killing of the colt, Gamut grieves in such a way that he commands the solace and respect of Hawkeye, who says that "it's a good sign to see a man account upon his dumb friends." In being thus cruelly initiated into the expediencies of savage warfare, the singing master temporarily loses his comic character to become the sad civilian, the inexperienced outsider on whom the magnitude of these actions can fall with full personal force.

CHAPTER 6

Summary

Heyward and the girls are uneasy and Gamut is still struggling in spirit when a light flashes upon them and they see that the others have entered a cavern hidden by a blanket. Hawkeye is holding a blazing knot of pine which silhouettes Uncas, the first clear sight of whose carriage and almost Grecian features relieves the lingering doubts of those from Fort Edward. When the latter also enter the cavern, they learn that at the other entrance is a narrow, open chasm running at right angles and that just beyond it is another cave. They are essentially on an island of rock with the falls and turbulent water on both sides.

As they take their meal of venison, Uncas makes an innovation on his Indian customs by attending the females, betraying a bit more interest in Cora than in Alice. In spite of his continuous vigilance, Hawkeye draws out a keg and invites Gamut to "try a little spruce." After they discuss Gamut's name and profession, the psalmodist and the girls render a sacred number that is safely muffled by the noise of the falls. The memory of his boyhood in the settlements brings tears to the scout's eyes just as the song is interrupted by a sudden, unearthly cry. In the ensuing stillness Uncas cautiously steps outside but can see nothing to identify the unknown sound.

Heyward takes the girls into the inner cave for sleep and inspects the far entrance to find directly beneath his feet an impenetrable barrier of roiling water. Though yet stoical, Cora seems for the first time to feel it rash to be trying to visit their father during this crisis. Heyward is reassuring the girls about Munro's feelings for them when the horrid cry fills the air again. Within a moment the blanket-entrance is raised and the scout stands there, his face reflecting everyone's fearful sense of mystery and his own growing dismay.

Commentary

This chapter shows Cooper in his most inventive, dramatic, and descriptive form. His sympathy and admiration for the good Indians ring through his own delineations and the appreciative words of Heyward, Alice, and Cora. By putting the poetic description of the island and falls into the mouth of Hawkeye, he reveals his deep respect for and clear knowledge of nature and at the same time deepens the characterization of the scout, whose sense of justice, relativity, and "place" is again highlighted when he admits that Gamut's "strange calling" is his "gift" and must not be denied. Completing and technically sustaining these developments are the plot elements of suspense and exploration of locale. Preparation for future thematic plot complications is smooth and unobtrusive in Uncas' brief attention to Cora.

CHAPTERS 7 AND 8

Summary
    Feeling that the cry is some kind of warning, whether intended or not, Hawkeye leads the entire party from the caves. As Heyward remarks upon the loveliness of the scene, the horrifying sound comes again as if from the bed of the river, and Heyward now recognizes it as the shriek of a horse in terror. The scout's reckoning that the horses are frightened by hovering wolves is immediately confirmed by a long howl that swiftly recedes into the depths of the forest, an abandonment that indicates enemy Indians are near. Once again secure in his knowledge of things, Hawkeye directs everyone to hide in moon shadows where they have a full view of both shores.

    Hours pass, and all fall asleep except the ever watchful scout and the Mohicans. The moon sets, and as pale dawn begins, the Iroquois attack with hellish yells and rifle reports. Gamut exposes himself, is wounded, and falls unconscious, while Hawkeye slips below and shoots one enemy, afterwards saying that their only hope is to hold the rock until Munro sends a party to help them.

    Heyward takes the girls into the outer cave where the reviving Gamut has been taken. As Cora reminds him how much his safety means to them, the major glances at Alice, reassures them, and rejoins the others outside. He and the scout deploy themselves in a little thicket of pines below the rock that splits the falls. Dawn comes. Then a long, anxious, and quiet watch succeeds until Hawkeye detects that four Indians have swum dangerously down to the rock above the defenders. As they wait, a fifth one, struggling to reach the rock, is thrown into the air and over the falls with a single, despairing shriek. After whistling Uncas to them, Hawkeye and the warrior shoot two Indians as the four charge them. When Heyward's pistols misfire, he and the scout grapple hand-to-hand with the two remaining enemies until Hawkeye dispatches his foe with a knife. Heyward is about to be dragged over the precipice with the other when Uncas severs the tendons of the Iroquois' wrist and grabs Heyward as the wounded savage falls to his destruction. As the survivors take cover, the Indians on shore yell and fire, and a give-and-take battle begins.

    One savage, who has climbed an oak tree near shore, fires down upon the protagonists and slightly wounds Heyward. Setting up a crossfire with Chingachgook, Hawkeye fires his rifle "Killdeer" and wounds the savage, who is left swinging in the wind with a desperate grasp on a branch. To save powder, the scout refuses to show mercy and finish the kill, but he weakens and discharges his last powder and bullet as the man falls toward the rocks and water.

Uncas goes for munitions in the canoe only to find an Indian swimming away with it. Now essentially bereft of defensive means, the Mohicans scoff at their enemies and prepare for death. Hawkeye is quietly and stoically preparing himself also when Cora, who has been brave all along, entreats the men to escape downstream and effect a rescue. Convinced of her reason, Chingachgook slips under the water and away. After telling her to leave a marked trail if they are captured, Hawkeye carefully lays "Killdeer" aside and disappears into the water. Uncas remains until Cora, lowering her eyes, asks him to go to her father as her "most confidential" messenger; then he also drops into the water. When Heyward refuses to leave on the grounds that his presence may keep the girls from evils worse than death, Cora draws "the nearly insensible Alice after her into the deepest recess of the inner cavern."

Commentary

While outwardly these two chapters are concerned chiefly with fright and action for entertaining the reader and multiplying difficulties for the characters, it also portrays the bloody cross-purposes of frontier strife: seven Iroquois are killed and two white men are wounded, while the male protagonists are finally confronted with a moral dilemma. Are they to face danger and probable death with calm, frontal bravery, or are they to turn to subterfuge and escape, hoping to effect a rescue but running the risk of being deserters? It is a bigger problem than that found in most sentimental novels, where woman's greatest threat is usually to her virtue or reputation. Here it involves the age old physical responsibility of the male for the female and — greater yet — of the strong for the weak, the typical assumption in the myth of the American frontiersman. The decision and resultant escape of Hawkeye, whose Christian reasoning is notably different from that of the Mohicans, is of a piece with the American self-ideal about necessity and the ingenuity of "finding a way out." The fortitude of Cora at this point is also consistent with the accredited strength of American pioneer womanhood; it is she who sees beyond the immediate grave situation to a possible desperate solution for which she femininely entreats rather than insists. Further, though Cooper's females only seldom do so, in this instance Cora takes on the three-dimensional qualities of a real woman character when, revealing a bit of her personal feelings and utilizing Uncas', she urges the subtle distinction about messengers which leads the young Mohican to escape also.

At his best Cooper is not a novelist who presses his thematic elements very hard upon his reader. But the preceding elements are in these two chapters, and so are others such as the rifle lore that Hawkeye voices during the battles. The two white men from Fort Edward are significantly wounded in this raw frontier condition that is new to them. Although as yet unaware of it, Gamut is already confronting what Hawkeye knows and, after the psalmodist is unconscious, voices: that "singing won't do any good with the Iroquois." Thus in the singing master religious idealism and reality are meeting head-on. Also, Cooper is very slowly and carefully developing the attraction between Uncas and Cora. The surplus sentimental heroine is gradually being paired with a hero, but it is an original pairing that involves the conservative idea of racial "place" and is to result in tragic complications. While the story moves along at a brisk pace with action and Indian customs such as the preparation for dying, Cooper is touching upon and getting ready to develop further more crucial aspects of the frontier situation in the New World.

CHAPTER 9

Summary

In the stillness that follows, Heyward finds it hard to believe what has happened, especially as nature seems to reassert itself with the song of birds. Nonetheless, they all hide in the cave, Gamut still addled and Alice trembling and weeping against Cora's breast. The major closes the inner entrance with the blanket and a pile of sassafras, then seats himself with a pistol clenched convulsively in his hand. Gamut sings "Isle of Wight," which is interrupted by savage yells from the center of the island as a rush of voices pours down the island. When a triumphant cry is followed by the shout, "La Longue Carabine!" Heyward for the first time realizes that his late companion was the celebrated hunter and scout of the English camp, and he feels certain that their friends have escaped.

As the Indians enter the neighboring cavern, the major peers out of his sassafras entrance, sees the gigantic chief, and watches as exultant warriors bring blood-stained brush from the other cave and unwittingly pile it against his entrance. Though the Indians' shouts indicate anger in seeing their own dead and disappointment at finding no prisoners or dead enemies, Heyward feels that perhaps now they are safe. However, just as Alice begins to offer thanks, the features of Le Renard Subtil appear at the other entrance and the major fires his pistol without success. There is only a moment of surprise before a clamorous rush captures the four whites, who are dragged outside and surrounded by the triumphant Hurons.

Commentary

With the woodsmen off the scene of action, this chapter presents the relative ineffectiveness of the "outsiders." As before, Alice is the sentimental heroine, trembling and ready to swoon so that she demands the attention of others. Gamut is still too much under the influence of his wound to learn anything from his situation yet; he mechanically follows his interest in song. It is notable that while Cooper continues to present him as a weak personage—a weakness consistent with his naivete as a comic Yankee character—he again credits the psalmodist with a singing voice so good that it can cast a spell even through a travesty of song. Heyward, still solicitous of the girls and especially of Alice, is seen as the determined but unsuccessful hero who is too much out of his element. Little is seen of Cora in the present action, but she remains a strong character in contrast to Alice.

By the end of this chapter the first segment of the plot pattern that Cooper works so well is completed: the pursuit, which was instigated earlier, has now reached the point of capture. What the reader can expect now are the possibility and difficulty of escape. Actually Cooper has already varied his pattern by letting three of the party escape before the capture. Plot thus adds hopeful suspense to the brutal threat of the obviously savage captors, made more threatening by the presence of the subtle Magua.

CHAPTERS 10 AND 11

Summary

Though at first menaced by the Hurons, Heyward is held for questioning; but he has to turn for interpretation to Magua, whom he sees Hawkeye had wounded on the shoulder. When he finally convinces them that the three woodsmen have escaped, they are furious, and one savage grabs Alice by the hair in a mock scalping. Before real violence can occur, the chief calls a brief council and the entire party crosses to the south bank of the river where the horses are. Mounted on Heyward's charger, the chief leads most of his people away across river, leaving the prisoners in charge of six Indians headed by Magua.

The major tries to secure Magua's help by privately implying that he and the redskin have been in collusion to fool the Hurons all along and by offering rewards. Although Heyward adopts the sententious speech of the Indians, Magua is noncommittal as the group heads south, the sisters mounted and the others afoot. Flanked by the Indians, Cora finds it difficult to leave signs on the trail; once when she drops a glove, she is detected and severely warned by one of their conductors. Never speaking, Magua steadily leads the way through the forests and hills until they finally reach a steep, pyramidal hill with a level summit and few trees—a perfect place for defense and for avoiding surprise.

While the warriors eat the raw meat of a fawn, Heyward again engages Magua in talk. Heyward's expression of Munro's love for his daughters brings a gleam of malignant joy to the Indian's face, and the latter insists upon a private talk with Cora. He proudly tells her that he was born a chief but that, after the Canadians taught him to drink firewater, he was driven from his tribe. Once when working for Munro, he came into Munro's cabin drunk and the latter had him tied up and whipped like a dog before the soldiers. He demands is it "justice to make evil, and then punish for it?" Wanting injury for injury, he says he will let Alice go if Cora will come with him as his wife: "The body of the gray-head would sleep among his cannon, but his heart would lie within reach of the knife of Le Subtil."

Cora is indignant and returns to her fellow captives. Magua goes to the lolling savages and begins a skillful harangue, building their emotions to the point of rage and vengeance. As they rush upon their prisoners with drawn knives and uplifted tomahawks, Magua villainously invites them to prolong the victims' misery. Heyward and Gamut struggle to no avail, and all four are tied to saplings while splinters and fire are prepared for the torture. Magua again makes his proposal, and Cora leaves the decision to Alice, who hesitates in her weakness but finally says no. Gnashing his teeth, the Huron hurls his tomahawk just above Alice's head, cutting some of her ringlets. Maddened, Heyward snaps his bonds and rushes upon another Indian who is about to throw his weapon. In the struggle Heyward goes down and the Indian raises his knife fatally. But the crack of a rifle is heard, and the Indian's look changes to vacant wildness as he falls dead on the faded leaves beside Heyward.

Commentary

These chapters are important for certain revelations and one presentation of *status quo ante* (prior state of affairs). The latter comes in Magua's explaining his past; his noble birth and his deserved but ignoble treatment by Munro do not justify his present actions, but they do make him and his conduct believable. They also raise the questions of justice and the big context of shared responsibility.

The revelations begin with Heyward's learning of the fame of his two former Indian companions, Chingachgook as "Le Gros Serpent" (The Great Snake) and Uncas as "Le Cerf Agile" (The Nimble Deer). Magua makes clear not only his motives but also the alternative routes that he will let his vengeance take. Perhaps the most important is Gamut's self-revelation when he struggles hand-to-hand with his captors: "David had contended, and the novelty of the circumstance held him silent..." The realities of frontier strife are beginning to impinge upon him.

Two influences on Cooper's fiction are also apparent. Indian lore comes forth in the figurative language of the natives, in the masterful and persuasive oratory of Magua, in the Hurons' contrasting silent patience and loud bloodthirstiness, and in methods of torture such as tying a man's arms to the tops of two bent saplings that will recoil in different directions. Sentimental qualities appear in the reactions of the fragile Alice, in the extreme testing of Cora's virtue and familial emotions, and in Heyward's over-vocalized sense of duty and honor.

Holding together all of these fictional elements is the plot device of the chase, through which a reversal of fortunes has occurred. Some of the pursued and some of the pursuers have exchanged their roles, while some have had relative security usurped by imminent danger and *vice versa*.

CHAPTER 12

Summary
Since the Indians' rifles have been placed to the side, Hawkeye has found his, loaded it, and fired it. He and the Mohicans advance to hand-to-hand combat, Uncas jumping protectively in front of Cora and saving her a moment later by killing an Indian whose tomahawk has cut her bonds. Soon all the Hurons are dead except Magua, who is fighting with Chingachgook. The villain feigns death and escapes before Hawkeye can brain him with the butt of his rifle.

Chingachgook scalps the dead while Uncas and Heyward assist the females and Hawkeye releases Gamut. The scout advises the singing master to give up his "little tooting instrument" for a useful weapon, and Gamut counters by arguing the fatality of Calvinistic doctrine found in books. Completely the practical man, Hawkeye disdainfully says that the only book worth reading is nature. Gamut's response is to sing a song, but Hawkeye common-sensically reloads his rifle and sees that everyone is armed. Then they start their journey with the girls riding the Narragansets.

They very shortly stop and clear the leaves and clay from a hidden mineral spring, and Hawkeye tells how the three of them, sagaciously aided by Uncas, had tracked the Hurons for twenty miles. After a simple cooked meal, they proceed towards the north where Fort William Henry lies.

Commentary
This is another bloody chapter, but its thematic significance is in the views of Gamut and Hawkeye. At first the psalmodist seems to have

learned nothing from his recent experiences; yet it is notable that, whereas before he has done little more than sing and mouth religious platitudes, he now turns to doctrine and argument as if he must go deeper into his beliefs to convince Hawkeye and perhaps himself. Although in this instance the Yankee's singing is a retreat as the scout gets the better of the discussion, Cooper gives Gamut his due as a folklore figure, "a minstrel of the western continent...after the spirit of his own age and country."

Hawkeye says that the recent action "was all foreordered, and for the best." But he will admit such only after events have actually occurred, not beforehand as Gamut's Calvinistic predestination insists upon. As something of a deist he reads God in nature: "I know not but man may so deform his works in the settlement, as to leave that which is so clear in the wilderness a matter of doubt among traders and priests." A few minutes later talking about the unusual way the Narragansets have been trained to walk, he comments that "natur' is sadly abused by man, when he once gets the mastery." His point is that man should not seek absolute mastery and try to rival God. Highly pragmatic, he finds that the greatest lesson taught by nature is humility. He is the noble, self-outcast frontiersman who has turned his back on the settlement to seek, as a thinking man, the freedom and simplicity of natural morality; and he prefers this even though (perhaps even because) it entails danger and killing.

Since Cooper is developing some interest between Uncas and Cora, just before mid-chapter he carefully presents Uncas as showing "a sympathy that elevated him far above the intelligence, and advanced him probably centuries before the practices of his nation." Though he will not fully allow it later because of the differences between savagery and civilization, Cooper is presently trying to make their mutual interest acceptable and believable.

CHAPTERS 13 AND 14

Summary
Now that the afternoon is shortening, Hawkeye leads the party many toilsome miles to an open space surrounding a low, green hillock crowned by a rude, decayed block-house, the scene of a victorious youthful battle for Chingachgook and the scout. Under the hillock are the long dead Mohawks, the memory of which makes Hawkeye once again refer to the two Mohicans as the last of their tribe.

All except Chingachgook fall asleep and awaken at the rising of the moon to continue their journey. Before they can leave, they hear the steps of some twenty enemy Indians who have apparently lost their trail. While the protagonists wait in quiet suspense, two Hurons approach the mound but warily withdraw out of respect for the dead. As soon as the sounds of the hunters completely fade away, the seven fugitives silently head north again.

After tactically walking barefoot in a stream for an hour, they turn again to the plain and reach the "bloody pond," where in a previous battle Frenchmen had been surprised, slain, and tossed into the water. Being now near the French outposts, they encounter a French sentinel, whom Heyward fools by answering in French and whom Chingachgook slips upon, kills, and scalps. Since they must turn back for safety, Hawkeye leads them up a mountain from which, as morning comes, they can see to the east Fort William Henry on the southern tip of Lake George. Between them and the fort are General Montcalm's ten thousand Frenchmen, while to the southeast is the camped detachment from Fort Edward.

Firing has already started, but as a great fog descends, the party plans to push through it to the fort. They have strayed from their way when a cannon ball from the fort rolls to a stop near them and they decide to follow its furrow to safety. Again running into French forces, they have to flee and become lost until Uncas finds the furrow again. They are hotly pursued, but within minutes they are beneath the walls of the fort, where Munro recognizes the voice of Alice and orders his men out the sally-port. Led by Heyward, the English disperse the French as the gigantic, grey-haired Munro, large tears rolling down his cheeks, folds his two daughters to his bosom.

Commentary

The story has now reached the end of the first long chase, during which one pattern of pursuit-capture-escape-and-pursuit is completed. But Cooper has made sure that the present safety for the main characters is only relative. He has made the reader aware that the defending English are far outnumbered and contained by the ten thousand French and their Indian allies; even the sentimental reader who may feel relief and a gush of emotional release at the reunion of the father and daughters knows that the protagonists now face the double danger of savage and civilized foes and can no longer maneuver as they did in the forests. If any lull is to come, it will be in terms of action, not suspense.

The action here is so intense that little individual characterization is presented. Gamut is barely present, and Uncas apparently has no chance to show his interest in Cora. At one point Hawkeye relates some of the history of the tribe of Mohicans, and his reference to his two companions keeps alive the background theme of tribal demise. But rather than its setting him apart as an individual, Chingachgook's taking of scalps merely shows how much he still has in common with all other Indians, though his actions do stand in contrast to the moment in the preceding chapter when Uncas rose above his native savagery. Hawkeye, who sees Chingachgook's actions as part of his Indian "gift," evinces one new character element with his superstition at the "bloody pond." However, since Cooper is busy rounding out his action, he does not dwell on theme or characterization in these moments.

CHAPTER 15

Summary

The siege is now almost five days old, and when in the afternoon Mayor Heyward repairs to the ramparts of one of the water bastions, nature seems to have resumed "her mildest and most captivating form." Two white flags indicate that a truce has been made.

The musing Heyward sees Hawkeye, bound and haggard, advancing toward the fort in the custody of a French officer. About to descend from the bastion, the major meets the two sisters, and Alice teases him for neglecting them. Cora says little and seems to be in anguish.

Heyward leaves to find Munro, who is now bitter and ironical because General Webb apparently is sending no help. While on message duty, Hawkeye has been captured and graciously returned, but the letter he carried from Webb has been kept by Montcalm, who has requested a parley with Munro. Instead, Munro sends the Major.

Montcalm is courteous and urbane, surrounded by officers and Indians, among whom is Magua, sullen and malignant. The French general reminds Heyward of the superior French forces and suggests a surrender, indicating that the Indians are hard to restrain. Heyward fails to learn anything about the letter and leaves carrying another request that Munro arrange to talk with Montcalm.

Commentary

Since this is a kind of interlude chapter, Cooper primarily develops the contrasts of the situation. Quiet nature now stands opposite to the human battles that have occurred and are still potential. Munro and Montcalm are shown with their differences of temperament as well as of nationality. In the French camp savagery and civilization, though temporarily

28

united, face each other as opposites. And the blonde-brunette contrast is seen in quieter circumstances than before. More than ever, Alice is the attractive flirt and Cora is the grave young woman bearing her unexplained anguish with fortitude. The usually resourceful Hawkeye, too, is in contrast with his former endurance and freedom; and his capture strongly objectifies the dire condition of the forces at Fort William Henry.

CHAPTER 16

Summary

Back inside the fort, Heyward finds Munro with Alice running her fingers through his hair while Cora looks on with amusement. The girls exit and Munro, refusing to talk of Montcalm, reverts to something Heyward had said when he first arrived five days earlier. He is very upset when he learns that the major had thought of proposing to Alice instead of Cora. He tells how, years before, he had gone to the West Indies and married a woman who was part Negro and who became the mother of Cora. Hence, because Heyward was born in the South, he thinks he is prejudiced though the young man denies it, having in truth known nothing of the situation. The commander continues telling how, after the woman's death, he returned to Scotland and married his first love, who died in giving birth to Alice. Munro is so distressed that Heyward says nothing until Montcalm's message is demanded of him.

They leave together for a parley with the French general, Heyward serving as interpreter. Montcalm reveals the letter in which Webb advises a speedy surrender of the fort. When the Frenchman explains his generous terms—the English are to keep their colors, their arms, their baggage, their honor—Munro accepts, though a permanent, progressive change in him begins immediately as he leaves Heyward behind to settle things with the French.

Commentary

While the surrender of the fort is important in terms of plot, Munro's revelation about Cora is more important for thematic purposes. It is to Cooper's credit as a writer that he has presented Cora well enough that the revelation comes to the reader in terms of recognition rather than surprise. Cora's black hair and slightly dark complexion, obvious all along, are the result of a racial intermixture on another frontier. Perhaps the anguish she showed earlier in the afternoon derived from the fact that Munro had misinformed her about Heyward's intentions, that she knew or was then told of her birth, and that she felt certain Heyward's interest was in Alice. Probably the fact of her condition or the knowledge of it has made her the calm, strong, enduring girl that she is. In any event, Munro was and is above prejudice and inveighs against the practice of slavery. On the other hand, Heyward, though he retains the highest regard for Cora, is rather glad that his attentions are toward Alice. Here at mid-novel the potentially tragic aspect of frontier life called miscegenation rises to plain view and, though at times dormant, will give an underlying sense of pathos to the remainder of the story.

CHAPTER 17

Summary

It is just before day on the 10th of August 1757, as a cloaked figure (Montcalm) emerges from the main French tent and moves beyond the farthest outpost to stand against a tree near the western water bastion of the fort. Just as the huge form of Munro appears on the rampart, the dark profile of Magua comes from the lake shore and raises a rifle towa d the Scotsman, but Montcalm stops him in time. Le Renard Subtil sullenly explains his reason for revenge, but he leaves, saying hintingly that he "knows how to speak to a Huron warrior."

French drums and English fifes start the day of evacuation. Heyward, who has to lead the troops, puts Gamut in charge of the sisters. Following the soldiers at some distance, the domestics are passing near the savages when one redman, thwarted in stealing a shawl from a woman, grabs her baby, dashes its head against a rock, and brains the mother with his tomahawk. Since Montcalm has failed in his promised escort for the English, Magua raises a whoop and the appalling (and historic) massacre begins, some of the Indians drinking the blood of their victims. Alice faints, and Gamut's loudly singing a psalm awes the Indians and thus keeps him and the girls safe until Magua, unable to find Munro, grabs Alice and dashes off, followed wildly by Cora. He puts the girls on one of the hidden Narragansets and leads it away as Gamut mounts the other horse and stays close behind. The Huron takes them to the very spot on the mountaintop where the protagonists had released the horses six days earlier. There they watch the massacre until the Indians finally turn to stealing and raising triumphant whoops.

Commentary

This is the bloodiest section of the novel and its outlines are a matter of history, though Cooper gives the instigation of it to Magua as part of his revenge. The contrast between savagery and civilized conduct is obvious, both in the incident at dawn between Montcalm and Magua and in the evacuation. In spite of his past experiences, Gamut is still the adult innocent, unable to see that the Indians are awed by what they think is boldness or madness rather than by the power of the psalm he sings. Like a character from a heroic play of the English Restoration, Munro is torn between duty and honor, but he passes by his pleading Alice to seek Montcalm and help for all; it is his last tragic act as a whole man, heightened by his disappointment when Alice faints. Magua, of course, is true to his base intentions, and it is thus through him that the second long chase sequence begins.

CHAPTERS 18 AND 19

Summary

On the third day after the capture of the fort, the area is one of stillness and death, the fortress a smoldering ruin. The August mists have unseasonably become an interminable dusky sheet driven by the tempestuous northern air when an hour before sunset five men — Hawkeye, the Mohicans, Munro, and Heyward — emerge from the forest and cautiously approach the ramparts, reacting with horror, shock, and stoicism to the confused mass of dead. Finding no signs of the daughters, they move around looking for a trail and Uncas discovers a fragment of Cora's green riding-veil. Other signs lead them to where the horses had been, and the party sees evidence that the girls, along with Magua and Gamut, have made off into the wilderness. Heyward wants to go in pursuit immediately, but Hawkeye says that they must deliberate and will spend the night in the ruined fort.

Munro has sunk into apathy as they arrange temporary accommodations for him and eat a frugal meal of bear's meat. The clouds break up and the foresters sit around a glimmering fire. On a rampart Heyward, looking out at the lake, hears low noises, calls the scout to him, and learns that wolves are on the prowl. Hawkeye presses a discussion of what paradise is like but is interrupted by another low sound and calls Uncas, who slips away. Chingachgook is warned and sits outwardly calm by the fire. A rifle shot disturbs the fire and Chingachgook disappears in an instant. A moment later they hear a plunge in the water and the report of another rifle. Uncas returns quietly to the fire until, upon Heyward's questioning, he exhibits the scalp of an Oneida, whereupon Hawkeye explains the division of mixed loyalties of the numerous Indian tribes.

Passing around a lighted pipe, the foresters quietly debate the next day's procedure, but finally and with Indianlike eloquence Hawkeye carries his point that they should head north by way of the lake. When he shortly goes to sleep, Heyward watches the Mohicans relax into pleasant familial informality. Then all fall asleep amid the ruins and the dead.

Commentary

At the beginning of this section Cooper steps in as author to comment critically on the massacre and on Montcalm. His description of the natural scene is masterful, his presentation of the strewn battlefield quietly horrifying, the reactions of the five men individually typical of each. Hawkeye cannot feel that any human beings are justified in such wholesale slaughter, but according to his belief in "gifts," he does accept the open fighting of a few warriors and even extends his acceptance of natural gifts to the ravens marauding the area of the massacre. Like Hawkeye, Cooper obviously feels that there are degrees beyond which human actions should not rightly go. Though Munro and Heyward and once Uncas wish instant endeavor, in reacting to the hasty and fatal events of the evacuation, the woodsmen now properly deliberate with calm their next move before effecting it. Once again Cooper has effectively made use of contrast, this time with incident against incident, haste against deliberation.

There are also two kinds of contrast in regard to the Indians. On the individual level the quietly laughing ease of the two Mohicans before they retire for sleep gives a new dimension to the father and son whom we have seen only as two upright and somewhat austere men during time of stress, and the scene invites a comparison with the one four days earlier between Munro and his daughters. On the more general level both Hawkeye's discussion and Cooper's explanation about Indian tribes contrast the present and past conditions of tribal warfare. Formerly an Indian could immediately recognize an enemy because of the rather simple opposition of certain tribes to others. Now because of Indian alliances with the French or the English, previous enemies find themselves side by side against a common foe one day and then perhaps opposed to each other later. Some like the Delawares are even divided among themselves, and the disorder of alliances is compounded because, as Hawkeye says, "it is natur' to give a preference to one's own quarrels before those of strangers." The result has been an utter "confusion of nations," a major stage in the dissolution of the original natives of the frontier area.

Hawkeye's discussion of paradise, a natural interest after viewing so many dead, stresses again his belief in individualism. While others may want a final place of rest, he wants a heaven of action and finds comfort in the fact that "we serve a merciful Master, though we do it each after his fashion."

CHAPTERS 20 AND 21

Summary

It is still dark when the party awakens and walks carefully on rocks, stones, and wood to the lake, where they shove off to the northward by canoe in a manner to leave no sign of departure. At dawn they enter the narrows of the lake with its numberless little islands. Discovering smoke in the mist above one of the islands, they make a push but are followed by two canoes of Hurons. They are holding a comfortable intervening distance when another war canoe starts across their course up ahead. By tacking westward they effect a parallel race with the new vessel and take the lead after being separated by an island. With enough distance to avoid the power of the Indians' short rifles, Hawkeye wounds a Huron with his long rifle "Killdeer," thus achieving escape when the enemy canoes converge and stop.

Upon reaching the northern shore, the men paddle eastward to deceive the enemy. With the canoe on their shoulders, they leave an obvious trail as they move inland, cross a stream, and reach an extensive naked rock. At this point they walk backward in their own footprints to the brook, paddle back to the lake, and, when darkness comes, safely reach the western shore where they conceal the boat and strike into the vast wilderness. After many hours of hiking, the travelers halt and for once sleep until the sun is up.

Uncas finally finds the trail of the fugitives, and the pursuers follow it to where it disappears in a much trampled area. They are at a complete loss until Uncas diverts the course of a little rill and fantastically discovers the impression of a moccasin in the streambed. Though Hawkeye knows that Magua's abandonment of the horses means that they are now in Huron territory, they follow the new trail and reach a point where they must deploy themselves to seek the enemy's whereabouts. Heyward is sent to the edge of the woods and there mistakes a beaver pond and its hundred earthen dwellings for a lake and an Indian village. Before he can signal the others, a rustling of leaves reveals a stranger Indian a hundred yards away. When apprised of this, Hawkeye makes a circle and is about to brain the stranger but instead taps him on the shoulder. It is Gamut made up like an Indian.

Commentary

These chapters are clearly devoted to the action of the new chase, emphasizing the dangers of frontier warfare and the subtleties of tracking.

Even the unbelievable discovery of the moccasin print in the rillbed illustrates the ingenuity of both the pursued and the pursuers.

Otherwise, only three matters of formality are presented. Even at the probable expense of danger and loss of time, Uncas is thoroughly deferential to his elders. During the battle of the canoes, custom will not allow Munro and Heyward to shield themselves by lying down in the boat while the others are exposed, and this foolishness stands in contrast to the practical advice and usage of the woodsmen. At the conclusion Gamut's admission that he might even try to teach the beavers to sing not only indicates his lack of profit from his frontier experiences but also reflects the dogged formality of his training and profession.

CHAPTER 22

Summary
Hawkeye is filled with merriment at Gamut, whose body is painted and his head shaved to leave a tuft of hair. The scout summons the others by cawing like a crow, and the singing master tells what has become of the girls. According to policy, Magua has separated his prisoners, keeping Alice with the Hurons and sending Cora to some Delawares in a neighboring valley. Gamut has been left to range freely because the Indians think he is, in Hawkeye's words, "a non-composser" (*non compos mentis —* not sound in mind) due to his singing. Hawkeye returns the "tooting whistle," which has been found on the trail, and knowing that Chingachgook himself is a great chief among the Delawares, comments that white men have done evil to bring the Mingoes and Delawares to travel the same path.

When the frontiersman suggests that Gamut go back to the Indians and let the girls know that help is near, Heyward firmly insists that he go also, acting a part. Using Indian paints, Chingachgook disguises him to look like a buffoon; with his knowledge of French, the major could pass as a juggler from Ticonderoga. Munro is to be hidden in charge of the elder Mohican, and Hawkeye and Uncas are to approach the Delawares.

Some two miles beyond the beaver pond Heyward and Gamut reach a clearing with fifty or sixty rude lodges. In the twilight they see fantastic forms alternately rising from the grass. They are startled but discover that it is only Indian children at play. Then they head for what Gamut calls "the tents of the Philistines."

Commentary
The motif of disguise, already foreshadowed by such procedures as imitating animals for signals, begins here in earnest and is to become a

highly important ingredient of the plot during the rest of the story. Closely connected with this in terms of technique will be lurid, frightening scenes reminiscent of the Gothic novel, begun at the end of this chapter with the grotesque, jumping silhouettes of the Indian children. Though according to Cooper's knowledge of Indians the redmen did venerate a "non-composser," such a view is a warping of the normal attitude of civilization. Conversely, the white man's temporary alliances with various tribes has disrupted the normal Indian order of things. All of these elements give a sense of the chaotic unreality of the frontier as Cooper sees it.

Ironically, out of this chaos has come the frontiersman, the ideal man. But the irony goes further because of the noble scout's "secret love of desperate adventure which had increased with his experience, until hazard and danger had become, in some measure, necessary to the enjoyment of his existence." Without the challenge, Hawkeye as Hawkeye could not exist. The situation is a prime instance of that mixed blessing that constitutes tragedy. Furthermore, when the frontier condition ceases, so inevitably must Hawkeye and others of his particular stature.

Cooper, of course, does not tell the reader this in so many words. If he did, he would be writing an essay. Instead, he uses the indirect and more telling method of fiction, in which meaning and significance are suggested by characters, actions, and situations.

CHAPTERS 23 AND 24

Summary
Typically the village has no guards, but the whooping of the children brings warriors to the door of the nearest lodge as Gamut and Heyward approach the principal building, brush past savages to the center of the lodge, and seat themselves in silence. In the light of a torch Heyward assumes the part of a French doctor and has to placate the Hurons, who feel deserted by the French. Shouts bring everyone outdoors where a war party has unexpectedly returned with several human scalps. In the lurid light from scattered piles of brush, two men stand forth, one erect and firm, the other with bowed head. The first is a prisoner who, surrounded at all perimeters, must run a hazardous race, either to escape or to reach a small painted post in front of the main lodge. The man shows remarkable speed and agility, but he is outnumbered and outflanked and finally reaches the post only when Heyward without detection trips the closest pursuer. The panting man is mocked and derided by the women but keeps his self-command, only once turning his head so that Heyward sees it is Uncas.

With all the principals inside the main lodge, a council begins. Through the capture of Uncas, the downcast young Huron has been caught in his third act of cowardice and continues to writhe in fright. Because of his acts, his aged father ritualistically plunges a knife into his heart, saying that his name is already forgotten. Immediately the torch is extinguished and everyone leaves except Heyward, Uncas, and the dead Huron.

Urged outside by Uncas, the supposed doctor wanders from hut to hut but cannot find any sign of Alice. Returning to the lodge where Uncas still stands and warriors are calmly smoking, he is about to be taken by a chief to cure a sick squaw when Magua appears. When Magua inadvertently refers to the cowardly Huron, there is silence until the father declares that he never had a son and leaves — in shame, for the Indians believe that virtues and defects in character come through heredity.

Magua surprises the others by identifying Uncas as Le Cerf Agile. He then orates for revenge on Uncas, and the Mohican is taken out to await torture and death the next morning. After Magua leaves, smoke fills the lodge again before the chief beckons to Heyward and leads him outside and toward the base of a mountain. They encounter a bear that seems relatively friendly but follows them closely as they enter a cavern. A glimmering light ahead directs them to a large cavity of many apartments where the Hurons keep their valuables and where the sick woman's bedside is surrounded by females and Gamut. Somewhat thankfully, Heyward sees that the paralyzed woman is beyond healing. Gamut pours forth a hymn and is so struck with wonder when the bear tries to imitate him that all he can say to Heyward is "She expects you, she is at hand" and exits precipitately.

Commentary

Cooper's fresh and original treatment in this section of the story leads to three variations — one in plot, one in motif, one in theme, and all involving Uncas directly or indirectly. In this second chase sequence pursuit has again led to a capture, but the difference is that now one of the pursuers has been made captive. Through the prisoner certain Indian customs are shown in the glare of grotesquerie, part of the motif of unreality that involves disguise, which shows its involvement here in the dissembling Heyward's tripping the Huron. Other Indian customs are the mocking of the prisoner, the scalps, the "death-halloo," and particularly the dealing with the coward. The death of the young Huron is reserved for the hands of the father who brought him into being, but it is traditionally an inexorable result. Thematically it presents a third father-child relationship and the end of a progenitive line. As Uncas is the last offspring of the Mohicans, the young Huron is the last male offspring of his family, but the difference is great. Whereas the Huron family's end comes from personal failure, the Mohicans' will come because men at large are responsible for there being only one potential Mohican father and no possible Mohican mother. The third father-child relationship is that of Munro and his daughters, and though Cooper makes no real point of it, it is more than obvious that, no matter what happens to the girls, the name of Munro ends with them. The end of a line is a very important theme in the overall purpose of the book, and in these two chapters Cooper adroitly integrates it with a major motif and the structural technique of the chase.

CHAPTER 25

Summary

Heyward wonders at Gamut's cryptic words but cannot think further on them because the chief sends away the women, turns toward his insensible daughter, and says, "Now let my brother show his power." After the bear growls fiercely three times and the Huron superstitiously leaves, the former removes its head to reveal Hawkeye underneath.

The scout tells that he has placed Munro and Chingachgook in an old beaver lodge and that, after Uncas' capture, he trussed up the tribal conjurer and donned the Indian's bearskin. Now climbing up to investigate further apartments of the cavern, he sees Alice and quietly slides back down. With water trickling nearby, Heyward washes off his paint so as not to frighten the girl, then climbs up to her, brings her up to date on events, and, in spite of their predicament, brings a look of innocence and surprise to her face by touching briefly on his feelings for her. A tap on his shoulder reveals the malign presence of Magua, who has entered by another door, which he bars and begins to taunt his captives. The growling bear appears, and Magua, recognizing it as the conjurer in whom he does not believe, brushes by it but is caught in an iron hug.

They tie and gag the villain and, since Alice is stupefied, Heyward wraps her in the squaw's clothes and takes her in his arms. Outside, where the squaw's relatives wait, the major says that he has shut the evil spirit in the cave and they are taking the woman to the woods to find healing herbs. The relatives are not to enter but to guard the door and beat the spirit back if it tries to escape.

In the forest Alice revives and Hawkeye directs them toward the village of the Delawares. He will stay to help Uncas. They try to dissuade him from so hopeless an effort, but he determinedly leaves them and moves back toward the Huron lodges.

Commentary

The motif of unreality continues, but underneath the disguise is something quite real: Hawkeye under the bearskin, Heyward under the paint. For the sentimental character Alice the disguise is too much. Hence the major washes himself, but the appearance of the bear, as well as the surprise and threat of Magua, is partly responsible for bringing on her almost senseless condition.

Her response, of course, also fulfills a demand of the sentimental novel. She has already had occasion to blush, tremble, and demur at Heyward's brief mention of his love and intentions. Her state of shock enables him to feel "the delicious emotions of the lover" as he carries her in his arms to the forest, and there her gentle struggles compel him "to part with his precious burden." The reactions of the two to each other are doubtless real enough, but their presentation is strictly that of sentimental convention.

In direct contrast to this presentation is the father-son feeling that Hawkeye has for Uncas. Both what he has given up and what he has gained as a frontiersman are poignantly revealed in his argument for staying to help Uncas:

> "I have heard," he said, "that there is a feeling in youth which binds man to woman closer than the father is tied to the son... I have seldom been where women of my color dwell; but such may be the gifts of nature in the settlements. You have risked life...to bring off this gentle one, and I suppose that some such disposition is at the bottom of it all. As for me, I taught the lad the real character of a rifle; and well has he paid me for it. I have fou't at his side in many a bloody scrimmage; and so long as I could hear the crack of his piece in one ear, and that of the Sagamore in the other, I knew no enemy was on my back... There is but a single ruler of us all, whatever may be the color of the skin; and Him I call to witness, that before the Mohican boy shall perish for the want of a friend, good faith shall depart the 'arth, and Killdeer become as harmless as the tooting we'pon of the singer!"

The sacrificial plight and the nobility of the woodsman are mirrored in his decision.

Along with this development of characterization and this use of sentimental convention, the structural technique of the second chase also advances. One person has been rescued, but two other captives remain; in fact, in a sense Alice and Uncas have simply changed places. It is yet to be seen whether the second element of the chase — escape — will be successful.

38

CHAPTER 26

Summary

Still dressed as a bear, Hawkeye returns to the camp and approaches a neglected hut in which he sees Gamut. Making sure the place is safe, he enters and seats himself on the other side of the fire, frightening Gamut until he reveals himself. Each one relying on the role he plays, they take a plain and direct route to the main lodge where Uncas is confined. Gamut tells the guards that the conjurer wants to blow his breath upon the captive to make him weak and fearful at the stake.

When the Indians fall back out of earshot, the two men enter and cut Uncas' bonds. With subterfuge necessary, Uncas puts on the bearskin, Hawkeye takes Gamut's attire, and Gamut bravely takes Uncas' place, planning to sing like a madman when he is discovered and hoping that will save him. Restraining themselves, the Mohican and the scout go slowly past the guards; but as they reach the woods, a long cry indicates that the deception has been discovered. Keeping faith that Indian superstition will save Gamut, Hawkeye finds their hidden rifles and the two men dash into the forest toward the Delaware village.

Commentary

Another part of the escape technique is now accomplished, and pursuit begins again. Disguise once more serves a useful purpose and, in the scene between Gamut and the bear in the neglected hut, it provides comic relief. Gamut is the butt not only of humor but also of irony when Cooper says that in his fright he "sought his never-failing resource in trouble, the gifted version of the Psalms." Basically Cooper is as practical as is Hawkeye, for earlier through incident and authorial comment he has cast doubt on the *intended* effect of singing psalms. The irony lies in Gamut's inability to understand Indians and the limited but certain way his songs *can* affect them. Nonetheless, in staying behind, the singing master does show bravery and strong gratitude for the help Uncas has formerly given him. When he does, Hawkeye's willingness as a relativist to reconsider things becomes clear: "I do believe your scent [direction] is not greatly wrong, when the matter is duly considered, and keeping eternity before the eyes, though much depends on the natural gifts and the force of temptation." This theme of relativity is also Cooper's as he demonstrates here and in numerous other incidents during the two long chases.

CHAPTER 27

Summary

Gamut sings loudly and the savages spare him because of his "infirmity." Almost immediately two hundred men are confusedly afoot, but a consultation is called. The real conjurer and the chief's dead daughter in the cavern are found and Magua is released, revealing to them La Longue Carabine — Hawkeye — has been in their midst. The enraged people send out additional pursuers and return to the council lodge. When runners report that the fugitives have gone to the Delawares, the chiefs speak in turn, Magua waiting until last. A good manager of people and situation, he orates well, and his view prevails when he recommends prudence. He has now regained favor with the Hurons and is placed at the head of affairs. Just as dawn begins, he leads twenty warriors in "Indian file" on an indirect route toward the Delaware village. One chief, whose totem is the beaver, pauses to address the animals as the group passes the pond. It is gratifying when one particularly large beaver sticks his head out of a lodge; but as the Indians move on, the animal removes its head and reveals itself to be Chingachgook.

Commentary

Other than moving the plot along through revelations that motivate the Hurons and other than the release of Magua which promises more suspense, this chapter's significance lies in the further characterization of Le Renard Subtil. He still has his individual motives for revenge on Munro and Hawkeye, but he is also concerned with something bigger and that is reinstatement with his people, generally villainous like himself. Since belonging matters a great deal to him, he must expiate the follies and disloyalty of his youthfulness; and now that he has helped his people by cultivating the Delawares, his oration and recommendations before the other Huron chiefs and warriors constitute his first major chance at expiation. Fortunately for him, he is a masterful orator and skilled thinker.

Cooper does not need, at this stage, to point the difference between Magua and Hawkeye, the villain and the hero, for it should be obvious. Magua takes on more depth and a certain amount of sympathy because of his desire to belong. Hawkeye, on the other hand, has renounced his people of the settlements but is more than willing to help them or anyone else who is worthy. He is good *per se,* the noble knight righting wrongs, and his attitude makes him an ideal. Thus while Magua rises above himself in a way, Hawkeye is already very much higher.

CHAPTERS 28 AND 29

Summary

It is morning in the village of the Delawares, who earlier withheld their assistance from their ally Montcalm. Though everything is peaceful, the warriors are apparently prepared to fight if necessary, for here and there they carefully examine their arms and eye a silent lodge in the center of the village. When Magua appears, unarmed and with a gesture of amity, on a near distant platform of rock, the principal chiefs meet him and he talks formally with their most approved orator Hard Heart. Unable to learn anything about his prisoner Cora and the "strange moccasins" of white men in the woods, he presents the chiefs with gifts. Sure of himself, he startles them by saying that the white man, who he believes is among them, is La Longue Carabine, the famous killer of Indians.

Calling a council of more than a thousand Delawares, they wait for the emergence of three aged men from a particular lodge. The tattooed patriarch in the middle is the famed Tamenund, well over a hundred years old. He is shown every extreme of respect and reverence. After a suitable delay, a few young men go to the silent lodge and return with Cora, Alice, Heyward, and Hawkeye. Uncas is not present.

To delay and protect the others, Heyward claims to be La Longue Carabine, yet so does Hawkeye. In a contest of proof, Heyward fires within inches of an earthen vessel at fifty yards distance; but the scout casually shatters it, and everyone believes it an accident. Hawkeye is convincing when he scores a bull's-eye on a gourd that the major barely misses.

After an effective oration from Magua, the hands of the scout and the major are tied. Cora rushes to the feet of the patriarch, but Tamenund, prone to sink into the lethargy of age, answers her supplications with facts about the wrongs done his people. Cora tells him that there is one of his own people who is not present but should be heard. Doubtful, the aged chieftain says, "Let him come," and sinks into his seat. In the deep silence, the young men prepare to obey his order.

Commentary

Racial conflict, consciousness of race, and pride in one's color—all give focus to these two chapters. Conflict is presented early in the discussion of the relationship of the Delawares to the French and to the Six Nations. It is objectified in the verbal fencing between the Huron Magua and the Delaware Hard Heart about prisoners and alliances and in the taunts thrown at each other by Magua and Heyward. But it reaches its climax in a revealing cry by the mixed-blooded Cora to Tamenund: "Like thee and thine, venerable chief, the curse of my ancestors has fallen heavily on their child." Cora, the strong, is aware of her background, and it is a sad weight upon her and a sore conflict within her.

Consciousness of race centers mostly in Hawkeye and Magua. When the former is handed the loaded rifle to prove his identity, he tells the Huron that he might now easily shoot him but he cannot—"because the gifts of my color forbid it." Magua makes profitable oratorical fodder of race by declaring that the Great Spirit made Negroes to be slaves and whites to be traders, but those with brighter and redder skins "did He fashion to his own mind." Magua's is a temporarily successful move to win the ethnic-minded Delawares to his side.

There is also pride in what Magua says, as there is in practically all of the formal movements and speeches of the Indians in these scenes. Tribal pride is seen in the Delawares' solemn delight in being called the Lenni Lenape, a people favored by the Great Spirit. The most sovereign pride is devolved upon the representative Tamenund, whose life has spanned more than three generations of warriors and who is a venerable living legend of both tribal and racial ancestry.

Underlying these matters of race, of course, is a continuation of the technique of pursuit through a variation. Here it is mostly a verbal tug-of-war for human lives, with Magua presumptuously pursuing and threatening because of the Indians' honor and tradition concerning a captor's right to possess his captives.

CHAPTER 30

Summary

Brought before Tamenund, Uncas is staunch and upright, proud and defiant in the knowledge that he is a chief and also a descendant of the Delawares themselves. When he laconically affirms that Magua is a liar, the patriarch turns him over to the Indians and the enraged Delawares prepare the dreaded trial of torture by fire. Uncas holds himself with serenity as a warrior tears away the Mohican's hunting-shirt and is rooted in frozen amazement at the small tortoise beautifully tattooed on the prisoner's chest.

The aged Tamenund, already shaken by the somehow familiar musical voice of Uncas, now thinks that he is confronted by the agile grandfather Uncas of his youth. With his identity and superiority established and acknowledged, Uncas cuts Hawkeye's bonds and convinces the Delawares that Magua has lied about him. Le Renard Subtil realizes that he is losing ground rapidly but insists upon his right to his prisoners. Questioned by Tamenund, Uncas declares that the men are not Magua's prisoners, but in all honesty he cannot deny that Cora is a captive of the villain.

Hawkeye partially offers himself in place of Cora, finally even saying he will throw Killdeer into the bargain, but Magua contemptuously will not agree. Cora says that she could not accept such a move and, bidding Alice a fond goodbye, she steels herself to go with the Huron. Both Heyward and Uncas vow to give chase when the sun "is seen above the trees," and with imprecations on his lips Magua disappears triumphantly into the forest with his prisoner.

Commentary

While making good dramatic use of Indian pride and customs in this chapter, Cooper also utilizes classic peripety — a reversal of fortune and circumstance. The occasion allows him once again — this time through the words of Tamenund — to touch upon the historic Indian trials and injustices at the hands of the white invaders; it is doubtless this history that has partly led the Delawares to believe Magua's lies about Hawkeye. The chapter further presents the scout's stoic fatalism when he rationalizes upon offering himself for Cora; and the tragic mixture of blood in Cora is reemphasized when, in parting with Alice, she touches her sister and says, "She is fair — Oh, how surpassingly fair!" The chapter, then, is one of reversal, revelation, and reiteration.

CHAPTER 31

Summary

Uncas watches the form of Cora until it disappears; then followed by a few warriors, he gravely retires to his lodge to meditate his course of action. When a dwarf pine is stripped of its bark and painted with red stripes, he emerges and begins a dance and war song to Manitou, the Great Spirit. Others follow suit, and they mutilate the tree as if it were the enemy. Meanwhile Hawkeye sends a youth to find his and Uncas' rifles in the forest, and the boy is undetected until he is almost in the village again; then he is shot at and slightly wounded by lurking Hurons, who are promptly chased off.

Taking twenty men unto himself, Uncas puts twenty under the command of Hawkeye and offers to do the same for Heyward, who declines. Reaching their scouts in the forest, they hold a "whispering council," and Hawkeye almost shoots Gamut when the latter approaches from the enemy side in his Indian attire. He informs them that the Hurons are between here and their village and that Magua has hidden Cora in the cave there. The scout now plans to take his men to the right along a stream to join Chingachgook and Munro at the beaver huts and then flank the enemy. After the two forces have extinguished the Huron warriors, they will carry the village and release Cora. Heyward likes the plan, which is immediately matured by their arranging signals and appointing each man to his station.

Commentary

Like the lull before a storm, this chapter continues with Indian customs of preparation during the honorary period of a truce. Also like certain parts in classic ballet or a symphony, the entire movement here is a ritualistic one of slow and relatively quiet potency. There are furthermore a few undertones of the epic, such as the preparation for battle and Uncas' encircling the post and repeating his song three times. Cooper's is a successful intention of giving dignity and religious overtones to a story that is to end in tragedy.

All of this is an intermediate prelude to another element of pursuit, the last of the novel. Loyalty of Indians to chief and of friend to friend is emphasized, and Gamut is brought back into the action because he can give needed information to the pursuers and because he yet has a significant developmental function to serve in the novel. It almost goes without saying that suspense is skillfully built.

CHAPTER 32

Summary

The forest scene is appealingly peaceful and quiet as Hawkeye leads his men many rods towards the rear where they halt at a brook and learn that they have been followed by the singing master. Having been reminded of a Biblical battle, Gamut is determined to join forces with the warriors in behalf of Cora. Hawkeye is doubtful even when the singer draws out a sling and picks up rocks for it, but the follower is allowed to continue with them as they proceed down the brook to where it runs into a larger stream near the beaver pond. They are advancing up the new stream when a dozen rifles go off to their rear and one Delaware falls dead.

In the furious battle that ensues, the Hurons fall back until Hawkeye's group is in an unfavorable situation. Fortunately, however, Uncas' forces open fire on the other flank. In the charge and hand-to-hand fighting that follow, the Huron contingent against Hawkeye's men is defeated and put to flight at the same time that Chingachgook and Munro come into the scene. As the rest of the fight comes up the hill toward them, the other Hurons are also put to flight with Magua conspicuously and rapidly retreating to the village. Managing to escape further, he and two fellow warriors dart off and enter the mouth of the cave, followed by Uncas, Hawkeye, Heyward, and Gamut.

The pursuers almost lose sight of the threesome but see the white robe of Cora at the far end of a passage that leads up the mountain. Rashly abandoning their rifles to go faster, Heyward and Uncas take the lead in following the Hurons and their hostage through an opening on the side of the mountain. On a precipice Cora refuses to go farther. Magua threatens her with a knife but is struggling within himself when one of his fellows stabs her in the bosom. Maddened, Magua springs for the Huron just as Uncas, leaping from a ledge, falls between them and Magua stabs him in the back while he is still prostrate. Arising anyway, the Mohican gathers enough waning strength to kill the murderer of Cora but is himself finished off by three more strokes of Magua's knife.

Heyward is too far away to do more than cry out, but Gamut from above flings a rock against the head of the other Huron and stands a threat to Magua, who leaps a wide fissure. Taunting his pursuers, he takes another leap that will make him safe, but he falls short and grabs a shrub on the verge. He has just gotten his knees on the edge of the mountain when a bullet from Hawkeye's rifle wounds him. There is a moment of suspense while Magua looks black defiance at his enemies; then his hold loosens and he falls to his destruction.

Commentary

The present action is the climax of the novel. The opposing forces are brought into tragic confrontation, and the final pursuit is ended. Once again, at the beginning of the chapter, Cooper sets up the quiet calm of nature to contrast with the bloody events that follow. By and large, though, Cooper devotes his skill to the exciting action that resolves the plot conflicts.

Among the surviving participants, Gamut's character shows the most development. Hawkeye is still the knowing woodsman, the frontiersman adept at pursuit and battle; but Gamut is finally taking on some of the characteristics of the frontiersman himself. Granted that he is yet the religious singer, but at least for the time being he has traded his "tooting instrument" for a weapon, his singing for fighting. When he is allowed to continue with Hawkeye's forces, his reply is that "though not given to the desire to kill, had you sent me away my spirit would have been troubled." Henceforth he is no longer bringing up the rear, and he actually fights. When he flings the rock against the head of the Huron on the mountain, the description that he thus "exposed the indignant and glowing countenance of the honest Gamut" is significant. For good or for bad, the singing master has at last come to active terms with the frontier condition.

Magua, too, is presented in fuller dimension than that of a simple villain. He is that, of course — evil, threatening, dangerous, and treacherous — but just as he formerly showed deep concern about acceptance by his people, he now demonstrates that his feeling for Cora goes beyond his original desire for revenge. When on the precipice she gives him no alternative (in light of his threat) but to kill her, he trembles "in every fibre" and is bewildered that he can only drop his arm without using the knife. What he finally would have done is not known, for the action of others interrupts his inner struggle. What is seen is that he is a man of complex and real emotions toward another human being. In his own right, he is a renowned chief early led astray by the firewater of white men. Part of the tragedy lies in the fact that the reader can see what Magua might have been under different circumstances.

The resolution of much of Cooper's thematic material remains for the final chapter of denouement. But he does give pertinent treatment of two major characters. And the fatal finality of the rapid action itself *is* thematic, the bodying forth of the tragic, conflicting differences bred of the frontier condition.

CHAPTER 33

Summary

The next morning finds the Lenape a nation of mourners in spite of their destruction of a whole community of enemies. Their own loss has brought sadness and humility, and everybody is outdoors in a silent circle about their dead. Munro sits desolate at the foot of the litter holding Cora's body, while nearby Chingachgook keeps a steady, anxious gaze upon the lifeless face of Uncas, now seated and dressed as if alive. After a brief speech from Tamenund, chanting voices are raised in honor of the deceased.

Beginning with the maidens, they sing that Uncas and Cora will be together in the happy hunting ground, that both are of sterling quality and are deserving of each other. But Hawkeye, who understands the Delaware language, shakes his head at "the error of their simple creed." After the warriors formally and in turn ask Uncas why he has left them, Chingachgook begins the monody of the father. Then the girls raise the litter of Cora and take her to her burial place where they cover the grave and Gamut sings from his psalm book. Munro asks Hawkeye to tell them "that the Being we all worship, under different names, will be mindful of their charity; and that the time shall not be distant when we may assemble around his throne without distinction of sex, or rank, or color." But the scout says that this will not do and merely thanks them. Afterwards Alice is brought from her mourning in a lodge, and all the white characters solemnly leave except Hawkeye.

A parallel ceremony disposes of the body of Uncas in Indian fashion, and Chingachgook makes a short speech ending with "I am alone." Hawkeye cries that it is not so: "if ever I forget the lad who has so often fou't at my side in war, and slept at my side in peace, may He who made us all, whatever may be our color or our gifts, forget me! The boy has left us for a time; but, Sagamore, you are not alone." The two woodsmen grasp hands across the fresh earth as Tamenund says that "before the night has come, have I lived to see the last warrior of the wise race of the Mohicans."

Commentary

The conclusion of the tragic story is befittingly somber and ritualistic, somehow bringing things together. For instance, Gamut, who has survived his initiation into the frontier, comes so under the spell of the ritual Indian singing that he submits to it and later adds his voice to the ceremony. The man who started out as the traditional, stock comic Yankee character has become in many ways the most thoroughly developing character in the book. He has experienced, learned, and gone into action both beyond himself and in spite of himself.

The motif of disguise (part of the bigger motif of unreality) has been dropped once the pursuit reaches the point of direct confrontation and action. Through death and its aftermath everything now stands out in naked reality. Chingachgook, for example, has discarded not only his beaver head but also all other decorations on his body except the one tattooed emblem as he faces his dead son. He and Hawkeye quite unashamedly shed tears over the grave of the youth.

The theme of miscegenation is also rounded out. What was apparently a taint of mixed blood for Cora is ended with her death, and through his grief Munro pays for his rationalized deviation. The further deaths of Magua and Uncas end the possibility of intermarriage between the novel's racial groups. If the reader assumes that Hawkeye is Cooper's spokesman, then the novel becomes in part a vehicle against miscegenation even after death. The scout's reaction is of course really an extension of his love for individualism and his critical relativity. He believes in a people's "gifts" and in keeping them pure. He respects the differences that confront each other on the frontier, and his view has become in fact a principle of differentness.

Cooper's big theme of the frontier has other aspects, of course, and again here at the conclusion of the story Hawkeye stands right at the center. In spite of (perhaps because of) his ideas about "gifts" and miscegenation, he reverences the concept of brotherhood. This is seen in his willingness to help any worthy person, in his relationship to Uncas and Chingachgook throughout the book, in his final words on Uncas, and especially in his symbolic grasping of hands with Chingachgook at the end. He is Cooper's ideal, stalwart man, in whom the two convictions — differentness and brotherhood — can survive side by side.

It is this quality in Hawkeye that gilds the edge of the cloudy tragedy. As the final words of Tamenund remind the reader, there comes an end for individuals, families, tribes, and even races. But in this novel Hawkeye embodies that which abides and, through abiding, overcomes. It involves what is ideal and basic to existence and, as here, it can reach the plane of symbolism and ritual.

CRITICAL ANALYSIS

In the *Edinburgh Review* for January 1820 Sydney Smith, the British denouncer of everything American, wrote disdainfully: "In the four quarters of the globe, who reads an American book?" At the time he was in general right, but by 1826 when *The Last of the Mohicans* was published, an honest appraisal would have been very different indeed. And no writer from the Americas was more responsible for the change than James Fenimore Cooper, whose novels were becoming about as widely read as were those of Sir Walter Scott, who has been credited as an influence on Cooper and with whom Cooper has often been compared. In order to extend a deserved appreciation to *The Last of the Mohicans,* the student will want to keep in mind two broad aspects of Cooper's unique situation as an American author: his status as a literary founding father and his native subject matter.

Cooper has rightly been called the first American novelist. Not that he wrote the first novel in the United States: that was William Hill Brown's *The Power of Sympathy* (1789). Neither was he the first to concentrate on the form of the novel, for in a remarkably short and productive period (1798-1801) Charles Brockden Brown had earlier turned out half a dozen full novels. But Cooper is properly heir to the title because he was the first American to make a life-long and successful career of writing novels and because his settings were mostly those of the New World, encompassing its social, political, and pioneer characteristics. Far more than any other writer up to his time, he fictionally presented the new nation and its background to the whole world, sometimes idealizing and sometimes criticizing.

As a dedicated writer without anything like a native literary tradition, Cooper was as handicapped as any of his American predecessors. Consequently he relied on tradition from abroad and developed some of his own from the setting and folk tradition of his native land. The former tradition can be seen, for instance, in sentimental treatment such as the overstated, coquettish, and stiltedly articulated love between Major Heyward and Alice Munro. But Cooper's sentimentalism is never as thoroughly developed or as strictly committed as that, say, of Hannah Webster Foster's *The Coquette* (1797), which apes Richardson's classic *Pamela* right down to its form, a series of letters. It is a surprising paradox when one realizes that *The Coquette* is based on actual events in Connecticut, with the fiction only a thin veneer; but the story as presented, far from relying on its setting, could easily be shifted to another country like England. Such is not true of Cooper's work. The quality of events in *The Last of the Mohicans* is as indigenous as Hawkeye's cap of skins and his buckskin leggings, which made the scout known the world over as Leather-Stocking. The love between Heyward and Alice, sentimental though it is, could not have progressed in its precise way except on the American frontier and amid the events peculiar to the frontier condition. Cooper is fusing an established literary tradition with something of his own as a member of a new, green, and hitherto non-literary nation. In the fusing, that which is new becomes primary, as can be seen in the conclusion of the novel where the perfunctory pairing off and disposing of sentimental lovers is almost lost from sight in such overriding concerns as the dignity, ritual, and tragic passing of the Indians. The bringing together of the foreign and the native (witness Hawkeye's "ability" at times to use rather literary language and at other times to talk in the strict vernacular) is sometimes an uneasy amalgam, but the good reader will be careful not to embarrass himself by taking Cooper too much to task. The alchemy of innovation often means that some fool's gold will crop up with the real metal, and it would be as unfair to criticize the Wright brothers for being unable to fly a jet airliner as it is to insist upon Cooper's writing like a modern American novelist.

For one thing, Cooper never meant to be writing realism. In the 1850 preface to the collected Leather-Stocking novels he quite sensibly answered his critics thus:

It is the privilege of all writers of fiction, more particularly when their works aspire to the elevation of romances, to present the *beau-ideal* of their characters to the reader. This it is which constitutes poetry, and to suppose that the red-man is to be represented only in the squalid misery or in the degraded moral state that certainly more or less belongs to his condition, is, we apprehend, taking a very narrow view of an author's privileges. Such criticism would have deprived the world of even Homer.

The term *beau-ideal* is a key one. Cooper is true to the spirit of the American frontier, but he is writing romance as distinguished from realism and naturalism. For his characters, even those rounded and relatively three-dimensional ones like Hawkeye and Magua, he abstracts in order to make them recognizable and representative. When we note that a Cooper Indian, for instance, is usually all good or all bad, it may be well to remember that Milton's Satan, though at times admirable, is all evil, his Christ all good. Both writers (and this is not to imply that Cooper is Milton's equal, for he certainly is not) abstracted certain qualities in order to present a world-view that was also a belief strongly tinted with tragic sadness. Cooper, who seldom did any rewriting, was far from the careful craftsman that Milton was; nonetheless, Cooper too, though working on a national rather than a cosmic scale, wrote of the sin of man and a consequent vanishing way of life and of an ideal human messiah image that could point the way to rectifying a bad situation. Cooper's was a lesser achievement than Milton's, but both men worked with what, from any broad consideration, must be called romance; and the novelist in fairness should be read in terms of what he intended to write.

Cooper, then, should be appreciated as a writer blazing new ground, an entertainer unable to divest himself of certain stock traditions like sentimentalism which had proved its ability to hold a reader, an artist slowly and with reasonable success experimenting his way into a new, native, and to-be-established tradition. He did this by abstracting from frontier rifle lore, from the Indian lore personally seen or found in the factual writings of the Reverend John Heckewelder and others, and, along with his own observations, from the history and the oral or written folklore about frontiersmen like Daniel Boone. What he did achieve is worthy of understanding and appreciation. Only that way can a reader realize how quickly Sydney Smith was proved wrong. Only that way can one properly withhold or offer applause.

PLOT

The motive force for a plot in fiction is always, it seems, one or more of three kinds of conflict: man against man, man against environment, or man against himself. Sometimes the conflict is so subtly treated that the inexperienced reader is at best only subconsciously aware that it exists at all. Such, however, is not true of Cooper's novel. Primarily the conflict is seen as man against man: whites versus Indians, Indians versus Indians, English versus French. More softly treated but nonetheless permeating is the looming fact that man is coping with the frontier, trying to conquer, tame, and possess it; it is this, in fact, which leads to the obvious conflicts of man versus man. And it is constant, the steady principle in all the variations of the man-against-man conflict. Without it or something very like it, the plot, no matter how skillfully attempted, probably could not come into being, and there would be no novel.

Having or discovering the prime motive force, however, solves only half the novelist's plot problem. This lifelike principle must find its way into some kind of active material substance. In the case of the fiction writer this material becomes such things as setting and characterization, which will be discussed below. The unifying element of activity and progression we call structure; when the writer structures his conflict(s), he has then realized and created his plot.

As was noted early in the Introduction, Cooper's overall structure is a simple one: two long chase sequences with a short, suspenseful interlude between them. Like any good edifice with its division into rooms, windows, etc., the novel's structure must be supported by constituent patterned details, the decoration of which will vary according to the taste of the builder or the taste to which he is appealing. Each of Cooper's chases, then, is patterned as pursuit-capture-escape-and-pursuit, a technique to which he gives vitality with variations such as letting the pursuers and the pursued change roles. Since, because of the great importance of theme, decoration may be as significant as anything else in the novel, it is often difficult to decide whether an element is pattern or decoration. From the limited standpoint of plot alone, however, we may hazard that Cooper is purposely decorating his supporting patterns when he regularly follows a scene of blood and violence with a calm scene in which the natural world reasserts itself as death is always succeeded by regeneration. Such presentations as Indian customs and rifle lore stand forth primarily as decoration, though they also give substance to the people involved or described. Even the characterizations themselves take on a decorative quality since Cooper only intermittently (with David Gamut, for instance) dwells upon developmental change in character. Thus in *The Last of the Mohicans* plot is a bit more complex and complicated than it at first appears: decorative form germinates within patterned form, which in turn germinates within the overall structural form. All of this, moving forward together because of suspenseful conflict which seeks and reaches a resolution, is Cooper's kind of plot here.

The overall structure gives a unity of plot movement, which progresses chronologically from day to day. Likewise unity of place is observed in that all the action occurs in the frontier area around Lake George and the headwaters of the Hudson River in New York State. The unity of time is compact, the total action occurring over a period of days from late July to mid-August in 1757.

In spite of these unities, however, critics' attitudes toward Cooper's plot have varied. An anonymous review in the *London Magazine* (May 1826) said this: "The story is a tissue of common-place Indian adventures, abounding with hair-breadth escapes and surprisals." Almost exactly a hundred years later Lucy Lockwood Hazard, in *The Frontier in American Literature* (1927), felt that "Cooper deserves less credit for his plots than for any other part of his romances." On the other hand, a champion of Cooper like Thomas R. Lounsbury, in *James Fenimore Cooper* (1882), while admitting certain improbability of action and insufficiency of motive in the story, averred that "the interest not only never halts, but never sinks." The complexities that we have already noted indicate that Cooper does deserve some credit for his plot. Probability, though, is an aspect that may warrant further exploration.

Readers generally will concede an author an improbability which gets his story going, provided that the resultant effect is compatible with and does not exceed the potentials of the initial causative situation or action. Cooper assumes this allowance when he lets Cora and Alice Munro insist upon visiting their father at Fort William Henry even though it is the worst possible time for a visit or a trip through the forests. He further presumes when he lets the small party strike out on its own through savage-infested territory rather than accompany the army. This is unreasonable action on the part of the characters and Cooper fails to give them sufficient motives for it, but it does get the story going in a suspenseful way that leads directly into the plot structure. In other words, it works if the reader will allow the initial improbability. In essence, it seems to me, all the resultant major events follow logically from this beginning.

Yet, some of the details of later events bear questioning. The hair-breadth escapes and last-minute rescues often seem fortuitous. But anything can happen in war; the unusual often becomes the usual. Furthermore, at various stages in our development we have appreciated such happenings in thousands of western and war movies because we tacitly accepted them as romance rather than realism. We might try doing the same for Cooper, since he was deliberately writing romance.

Perhaps other occasional events are harder to swallow, particularly the one in which Uncas turns aside a small stream and finds there a moccasin print that leads the woodsmen on to Magua. Though Mark Twain was not the first to criticize this occurence, ever since he ridiculed it in the *North American Review* of July 1895, it has too often been accepted as typical of the book; but such is simply not true. Twain's satire called for exaggeration and was based on the demands of realism rather than romance; the satirist furthermore inaccurately stated that it was Chingachgook who turned aside the stream. This one event is, of course, fantastic and impossible; but it is the most flagrant one in the novel, and there are rather few other, lesser ones. While it would be better omitted, it is not representative of the novel as a whole.

In looking at the plot of *The Last of the Mohicans,* the reader will do best to appreciate Cooper's genuine art of improvisation and to remember that the plot is one of romantic action, the background of which is the wresting of a continent from nature and the Indians.

SETTING

Cooper's setting is that of the American frontier with its physical background of wild and virgin nature, its human cross-purposes and conflicts. It is a place of primeval forests, mountains, caves, and waterfalls; a place of great beauty and of constant potential threat from its terrain and its native Indians; a place where a man, if he chooses, can be a Deist letting religion be "revealed" to him through nature and his own reason, sacred writings being unnecessary. But the time is that of the American pre-revolution (1757) when white men are exploring and ruthlessly pushing westward. Thus man, though in general an inextricable part of nature, becomes a blot on what nature would be without him on its landscape, for man feels he must possess — must own — nature physically whether he does so spiritually or not. Human nature exerting itself at this time and in this place generates Cooper's setting, the American frontier in New York State.

Human nature, of course, is not all bad. Though most men in the novel seem to be caught up, either directly or indirectly, in conflict for holding or gaining the land, there is Gamut who is ineptly concerned with religious values, and there is especially Hawkeye who does possess the landscape spiritually and who despoils its produce (plant, animal, or man) only to defend or feed himself. But these two are doomed to failure: Gamut because he is too narrow-mindedly conventional ever to understand another culture enough to reshape it, Hawkeye because (even if Cooper had never made it eminently clear, as he did, in other novels of the series, especially *The Prairie*) it is obvious in *The Last of the Mohicans* that the frontier condition will finally pass off the scene and carry with it the man and his virtues which that condition fostered. This is clearly indicated by the recurrent theme of finality which gathers like darkness at the end with the Indians being slowly dispossessed of land, sustenance, and existence. The civilizing white invaders are already winning. The setting, then, is not merely that of time and place (though these are historical, convincing, and necessary to the novel's basic reality about life) but is also one of atmosphere, that aura which encompasses, permeates, and unifies — and somehow at the same time comes from — all the living elements of a novel. In this case it is the atmosphere of conquest and dispossession.

Critically one can easily isolate the time and place of the novel, but doing so with atmosphere is less easy because atmosphere is intimately intertwined with all aspects of the novel. Lucy Lockwood Hazard, in *The Frontier in American Literature* (1927), is very close to my meaning when she says: "The frontier affords the setting; it occasions the plot; it offers the theme; it creates the character." After a reader mentally vivisects the novel to examine its parts, such as elements of setting, these parts come back together for him with new focus, scope, and meaning in a thematic atmosphere for which we fortunately have the name of American frontier.

CHARACTERS

With the relatively minor exceptions of David Gamut, Colonel Munro, and Uncas, the characters in *The Last of the Mohicans* are static ones. We learn more about them as the novel progresses, not because they develop within themselves, but because through their talk, actions, descriptions, and sometimes authorial comment Cooper reveals more about them to us. Many American writers — Hawthorne, Melville, Hemingway, and others — emphasize change in character, with concentration on growth and development. Why does Cooper do so little with this?

One reason is the influence of the sentimental novel in which a character and his desires, even when fulfilled, are approximately the same. He begins and ends with these concerns, these needs in the face of difficulties which must be and usually are overcome. Thus Major Heyward remains the same throughout, always, in relation to the frontier, the outsider primarily aware of his love for Alice; he undergoes no change from his frontier experience, and his attitude toward miscegenation is unaltered although it involves someone very close to him indeed. Other features of stereotyped sentimentalism abound: the delicate, flower-like Alice Munro swoons at the most inopportune times of crisis; her beloved Heyward sometimes postures and blusters with the best of intentions; the conflict between absolute good and absolute bad is sometimes too obvious and pat. Sentimentalism, however, does not explain the static quality of more important characters.

A much more significant reason is Cooper's belief in "place." As a son of eighteenth-century rationalism, he accepted the concept of stratification is both society and government. It is true that he believed in the ascendency of the uncommon man, but this man was to better himself within his own stratum. Within his limited state—his freedom of individuality —he might even prove himself more worthy than someone socially above him. It is thus that Hawkeye, the most comprehensively noble personage in the book, always defers to the superior social and military rank of Colonel Munro, who proves himself unable to cope with the situation. Though it does not necessarily have to have such control over characterization, this concept of "place" probably was the most important reason for Cooper's static characters. While it is for Cooper an up-to-date and rational idea, it has its parallels with the ancient physiological theory of "humours," those four chief liquids of the human body which were believed to determine character. Substitute Hawkeye's emphasis on people's "gifts" for the belief in "humours," add the great variety that the subtlety of rational stratification would allow, and one may well come up with Cooper's static view of characterization in which it is more important to show what a man is like—and hence what his "place" is—than to show how he may basically change.

What of the characters that do show some change? Throughout the commentaries we have noted that the one evincing most potential for change is Gamut. He begins as a stock comic Yankee, as ungainly a putting together of arms, legs, body, and dress as Irving's Ichabod Crane of 1820. He is the only really unmanly male in the book (if we discount the cowardly young Huron, a very minor personage). He is a dedicated, simple-minded, blindly blundering psalmodist whose abrupt contacts with frontier realities give him pause to reflect. At the end of the story he develops a belated manliness in giving chase and pathetically offering battle, in the final scene succumbing to the chanting of the grieving Delawares. In spite of the extended, intermittent presentation of his development, however, Cooper never quite convinces that there is any real inner change (Gamut's going into battle, for instance, is motivated as much by his seeing in it a Biblical parallel as by anything else). Colonel Munro's change is only that of a man whose disappointment and grief are rapidly making him senile. Once Cooper points to Uncas as an Indian coming close to losing some of his savage condition, yet the cause is not civilization but his growing interest in a woman. At best the change in him is only partial, and that is shown mostly through instinctive deferential good manners toward Cora. Two of these characters, then, indicate potential inner change, but all three reveal only outward manifestations. In none of them is there anything like an inner development that means a rebirth of his essential being.

Among the other noteworthy characters, Cora Munro, though she indicates some timid affection for Heyward and some cautious interest in Uncas, goes beyond the usual sentimental heroine. She takes on depth because of her moody nature and her innocent involvement in miscegenation, but she too does not develop within herself. Chingachgook throughout is the quiet, stoic, and noble Indian who has been dispossessed of land and tribe. He is a chief (one notes that when he joins the battle near the end, Hawkeye relinquishes to him his "place" as rightful leader of the armed Indian band) whose sadness and loss are intensified, not altered, by the final turn of events. The venerable patriarch Tamenund, who does not appear until late in the novel, is nonetheless significant as an Indian who, in growing very old, has watched and felt the decimation of his race. Much as in a Shakespearean tragedy, he, as the most important personage left on the scene, gives the final, summary oration. Yet his too is a static characterization.

Magua deserves separate consideration as perhaps the second most important persona in the novel. He is the archenemy in whom all the evil side of savagery is illustrated. Other bad Indians are common but are usually in the background or come to the fore only occasionally. Magua is a constant threat, motivated by revenge, a man of great strength and cunning. He is an individual in his own right, pursuing his personal cruelty and desires, but he is also representative. As such, he embodies the salient attributes of savage evil, yet he is not merely evil. Within his way of life, his is a worthy ambition to reinstate himself with his people, to regain a chance to lead an existence that to him is noble and right. His real attitude toward Cora is revealed in his final inability to kill her and his immediate attack on the man who does stab her to death. Since Magua, who represents the evil Indian, is not all bad, he stands as a caution against a too easy assumption that Cooper invariably separates his Indians into the good and the bad. As an antagonistic character seen mostly from across the line of conflict, Magua is yet one of the best developed ones in the novel.

The most important character, of course, is Hawkeye. He has already been described in the Introduction, so that here we can dwell upon what he stands for. He is the mythic hero, the true democrat who accepts everyone according to his "gifts" and differences but who, because he is (as D. H. Lawrence has described him) a saint with a gun, will right wrongs and avoid evils when possible, destroy them when necessary. He is a solitary in spite of his companionship with Chingachgook and Uncas, and he is such because he is the flesh-and-blood incarnation of the natural moral law. That is, he stands single above both savagery and civilization in that he contains within himself the best of both; he can, for instance, see that justice is a constant and bigger principle than any man-made laws, whatever good or bad society they may spring from. He has been thus elevated by going to the source of principles, that interconnected source which is simultaneously within nature, within himself, and within the relationship between himself and nature. This elevation is why he is an ideal human messiah image, for he stands revealed as a way of earthly salvation, an upright man among frontier strifes, a man with a coonskin cap instead of a halo. While he is an ideal, he is also a human being. He is garrulous and sometimes fussy about things like firearms and tracking. He is almost irritating about the certainty of his marksmanship. But he can also be humble and retire into the background with real modesty. He is, in short, a messianic mythic hero who is also a recognizable man.

All of Cooper's personages, while they generally act in keeping with their characters, are primarily static. Reasons for this may be found in the influence of the sentimental novel and in Cooper's concept of "place." But this characterization may also be part of a bigger plan, though Cooper may have felt rather than known the plan. These static characters function within a total situation that is one of dynamic change. They are caught in something far larger than themselves as a group or as individuals. The frontier conflicts are born of a more encompassing continental movement which projects its dynamism with additional strength simply because it rests in subtle contrast to the outwardly active but inwardly static characters. They are static as individuals, active as parts of a dynamic whole.

THEME

In considering theme, one may well keep in mind Marius Bewley's apt statement in *Major Writers of America,* Vol. I (1962): "The novels of Cooper are an exercise in national definition." In *The Last of the*

Mohicans the national phase being defined is the frontier, a major theme composed, like the plot, of significant constituent parts. Enough about the frontier has perhaps been said already, so that all is needed is a reminder that it is a place and a condition where differences meet head-on and often result in conflict. Since conflict is a basic ingredient of the frontier in the novel, the story's action of flight, skirmishing, disguise, warfare, etc. literally becomes theme. Rather than to illustrate something else, the conflict is meant to illustrate — that is, *be* — itself.

Embodied in the various elements of conflict is something sad and tragic — and universal. Revenge similar to Magua's may be found anywhere and at any time. So may the problem of divided loyalties, though seldom on such a scale as that of the nations of Indians. Conflict rarely ends in a lasting stalemate, and this fact is given tragic emphasis in the thematic passing of the Indians from the American scene. Although man's natural, instinctive urge to mate and procreate might at first appear as a possible solution to the problem of differences, miscegenation also seems doomed to failure since it compounds differences by isolating individuals even more from their backgrounds, particularly isolating any offspring like Cora. (This very view, along with his great respect for individualism, may have been greatly responsible for Cooper's voiced opposition, through Hawkeye as a spokesman, to miscegenation.)

Cooper's treatment of his theme is not all negative. The solution to these differences is to accept them and thereby rise above them. This answer is an ideal one, at best only seldom realized; and that is why Hawkeye, in his role as a messiah figure, is a mythic hero. What he embodies is great and potentially generic, but so far it has usually been beyond the full realization of men. It is the ideal of universal brotherhood, of loving acceptance of others with their individual "gifts." In treating this concept, which of course extends further than any frontier condition but is inherent to it, Cooper does not let his idea of "place" limit him to mere description and action. Instead, he unobtrusively but clearly points to nature as the most influential force in making Hawkeye what he is. The scout has little regard for organized religion and its books. In fact, in Chapter XII he says he has never read but one book, the book of nature, "and the words that are written there are too simple and too plain to need much schooling, though I may boast that of forty long and hard-working years." His eagerness to talk about religion and the hereafter even at highly inopportune times indicates his interest in the matter, but he is what he is and believes what he does because for forty years he has been instructed by nature. Part of the answer, then, is simplicity and fundamentalism, both of which are implicit, for example, in the recurring father-child motif. Hawkeye does not find his needs answered in the usual love between the sexes, but in a vicarious father-child relationship with Uncas (see Chapter XXV). Like the story's real fathers (including the father of the cowardly young Huron), he accepts responsibility toward the other with his differences in a way that is redolent of his brotherhood with Chingachgook. The splendid isolation that is his stems from his charitable and humane individualism, which paradoxically binds him closer than usual to others. Because this is a pure ideal, investing a fictional human being with it makes that person a myth. It is nonetheless worthy of mortal pursuit, and Cooper's presentation of it in *The Last of the Mohicans,* while by contrast it deepens the sense of man's tragic failings, functions like a thematic image of hope.

TECHNIQUE AND STYLE

Cooper's technique is the use of repetition, oppositions, and contrasts, the elements of each being quite clear and identifiable. Repetition is seen most obviously in the plot device of the trap and escape of the sympathetic party of characters, but it is also used effectively to drive home the plight of the Indians and the historical events that have brought them to their present condition. Some repetition is incremental — that is, it restates but with a difference, with something new added. This is true of Indian and rifle lore, of the miscegenation theme, of motifs like the father-child one and that of disguise. At its best the redundancy furnishes emphasis to something that Cooper feels is important; at its weakest it amplifies material (folklore, for instance) in which Cooper is interested or feels that his reader will be interested.

Oppositions abound and afford numerous frontier clashes: French against English, Indians against Indians and against whites, Magua against Hawkeye's party. In one instance of the father-child motif the Huron father, in admitting and accepting his son's differences that are negative to the tribal code of conduct, finds himself honor bound to oppose and kill the young, unprotesting warrior. At times opposition takes the form of debate such as Hawkeye's arguing religion with Gamut or procedure with Chingachgook and Uncas. The major and controlling opposition in the novel, of course, is that between savagery and civilization.

The most looming contrast in the novel is that between the condition of nature and the condition of man. Cooper is so effective with this that his following violent and bloody scenes with calm interludes of the natural world reasserting itself becomes a kind of ironic rhythm. In the realm of man itself are contrasts of cruelty with nobility, of hate with love. The

Munro sisters make a blonde-brunette contrast from without, while within Hawkeye rest contrasts between his inherent isolation and his sporadic involvements with others and between his reverence for life and his ability and occasional delight in killing.

Similar to his technique, Cooper's style is a simple one. He uses the figurative language of simile and metaphor sparingly, so that his exposition and description are usually factual and straightforward. Nonetheless his diction is sometimes wordy. He writes that "David (Gamut) began to utter sounds that would have shocked his delicate organs in more wakeful moments" when all he needs to say is that "Gamut began to snore." At other times the diction may cloy. For instance, when Heyward and Hawkeye (disguised as a bear) take the reviving Alice to the safety of the forest, Cooper writes this sentimental verbiage:

> The representative of the bear had certainly been an entire stranger to the delicious emotions of the lover while his arms encircled his mistress; and he was, perhaps, a stranger also to the nature of that feeling of ingenuous shame that oppressed the trembling Alice.

Such stylistic lapses, fortunately, are overbalanced by general lucidness, Cooper's delineation of nature often achieving poetic simplicity. His description of action—Hawkeye's competitive shooting to prove his identity, for instance—can be as clear and accurate as a stated fact:

> The scout had shook his priming, and cocked his piece, while speaking; and, as he ended, he threw back a foot, and slowly raised the muzzle from the earth: the motion was steady, uniform, and in one direction. When on a perfect level, it remained for a single moment, without tremor or variation, as though both man and rifle were carved in stone. During that stationary instant, it poured forth its contents, in a bright, glancing sheet of flame.

It would be difficult to improve these sentences for clarity and economy without losing the meaning and drama of the situation and action. Cooper's punctuation is sometimes erratic by standards of today, but his sentences— even the overstated ones—are always clear as to meaning.

His use of dialogue is another matter. Hawkeye's talk varies awkwardly from the literary to the vernacular, though his subject of discussion sometimes accounts for the verbal difference. Conversation of other characters is often stilted or too formal under the circumstances. In the case of the Indians, Cooper was attempting to imitate their figurative oratory in formal situations as he understood that declamation to be. Perhaps the kindest we can be to him is to say that he apparently lacked an ear for the rhythms of human speech in ordinary situations.

Finally there is the consideration of symbolism. Aside from the mythic symbolism of the scout, Cooper does not do a great deal with symbols. Caves serve a vital function for plot and setting, but they never conjure up the image, say, of Plato's cave or of the classic myth of the Labyrinth; and it would doubtless be stretching matters too far to find Freudian meaning in them. Some critics have felt that Hawkeye's description of the falls in Chapter VI constitutes a symbol for the occasional chaotic tumults along the river of life and thus represents the period of human conflict and chaos in the novel. Such is an ingenious and very tempting reading of the passage, and it does no violence to the import of the novel as a whole; but if Cooper consciously or unconsciously meant it to be a symbol for the novel, one might expect him to revert to the same or a parallel image now and then, especially near the end of the story. When he wants a reader to be aware of symbolic possibilities, he is generally as straightforward as with his exposition and description. When at mid-novel the five protagonists return to the scene of the massacre, for instance, Cooper says that the landscape, which had appeared different before, now looked "like some pictured allegory of life, in which objects were arrayed in their harshest but truest colors, and without the relief of any shadowing." We may say that, with the great exception of the mythic Hawkeye, Cooper's use of symbolism is rather haphazard and inadequately developed.

Cooper's major failing is probably in his style. It can be wordy, heavy, and awkward. But it does have the virtues of simplicity and clarity, both of which are appropriate for his plot, setting, and characters, and both of which make bas-relief of the frontier chaos, ugly and carbuncular against the healthy life of nature, nature's influence, and nature's Hawkeye.

GLOSSARY

Algonquin
The Indians of Algonquin stock were patrilineal, and their earliest home was north of the St. Lawrence River and east of Lake Ontario. At one time they comprised fifty to sixty tribes with many minor groups.

Delawares
The Delaware Indians, of Algonquin stock, were found along the drainage of the Delaware River and the shores of Delaware Bay. They called themselves ˋenape or Leni-Lenape and were actually a confederacy

of three Algonquin tribes—the Munsee, Unami, and Unalachtigo. After they were conquered by the Iroquois in 1720 and had their land encroached upon by the English, they slowly moved west via Pennsylvania, Ohio, Indiana, Missouri, Texas, and Kansas to Oklahoma. Though not particularly powerful or aggressive at discovery, they were accorded an honorific preeminence by other eastern Algonquins and were called "Grandfathers."

Hurons

The Hurons, matrilineal clans living originally near the St. Lawrence River, were enemies of the Iroquois and were among the first to receive the French as friends. After their confederacy was destroyed by the Iroquois in 1648-1650, they scattered and drifted, often in alliance or conflict with other tribes.

Iroquois

The Iroquois stock was divided into totemic, matrilineal clans with tendencies toward confederacies. Made up of some fifteen tribes with many minor subdivisions, these Indians' earliest home was somewhere between the lower St. Lawrence and Hudson's Bay as well as in southern Ohio and Kentucky.

League of Six Nations

The Iroquois proper of history comprise the Mohawk, Oneida, Onondaga, Cayuga, and Seneca tribes. The Tuscarora of North Carolina voluntarily moved to New York and about 1715 were admitted to the confederacy, which became known as the League of Six Nations. According to history, the League sided with the British against the French and other Indians.

Mingo

Mingo was a Delaware word that literally meant "stealthy, treacherous."

Mohican

This is apparently Cooper's composite name from two different Algonquin tribes—the Mahicans of the Hudson River Valley between the Hudson River and Lake Champlain, and the Mohegans from along the Thames River in Connecticut.

QUESTIONS FOR STUDY AND REVIEW

1. Is *The Last of the Mohicans* a unified novel? If so, where does the unity lie — in the plot, the characters, the setting, the theme, the style, the mood?

2. To what extent does the story rely on actual historical events? What percentage of the story would you say is fictional?

3. Look up the term *Gothic novel* and determine whether any major elements of that form are used in *The Last of the Mohicans*.

4. Discuss the extent and validity of symbolism in the novel. Can you make a case for Glenn's Falls (Hawkeye's description in Chapter VI) as a major symbol? Consider, for instance, that an Indian enemy plunges to death at the Falls and another, Magua, similarly goes to his destruction near the end of the novel. Do these two events make a parallel?

5. Explain how Cooper succeeds or fails in making Hawkeye both a believable human being and a mythic symbol.

6. What are the primary features of the frontier as a place? As a condition?

7. Among other contrasts in the novel is the blonde-brunette one of the Munro sisters. Does this in any way correspond with their fates?

8. Give some reasons why the novel must be classed as romantic rather than realistic or naturalistic.

9. How many characters in the novel can you describe convincingly as sentimental?

10. What exactly is miscegenation? Point to specific instances in the novel which indicate Cooper's attitude toward the problem.

11. Compare and contrast Gamut's and Hawkeye's concepts of fatalism.

12. Very occasionally Cooper makes use of humor. What seems to be its function in the novel?

13. Describe some events in the plot which show man pitted against his environment.

14. Justify one's calling Cooper the first American novelist.

15. Who are the most important characters in the novel? Explain their importance in terms of plot and theme.

16. What is meant by Cooper's concept of "place"?

17. How many father-child relationships are there in the novel? What do they have in common? How do they differ?

18. To what extent does Cooper make a simple division of his characters into the good and the bad? Does characterization suffer because of this?

19. Why is Hawkeye ultimately a doomed character?

20. What is the basic structure of the novel? Is it in any way mathematical or geometric?

21. Give some instances of Cooper's talent for improvising. Are these instances in conformity with the novel as a whole?

22. Why do you suppose Cooper gave the novel its particular title? Do the events justify the title?

23. Because of his treatment of Gamut and characters in other novels, Cooper appears to be skeptical about men of the Puritan tradition from beyond the mountains of western Connecticut and Massachusetts. Is Cooper free from that tradition himself? As a lead, what is the sin which Hawkeye, as a messiah image, illustrates can be rectified?

24. Cooper, like others of his time, believed in the idea of progress. Does *The Last of the Mohicans* suggest that he had any doubts or qualifications concerning that idea?

25. *The Last of the Mohicans* has been termed an American classic. Can you present reasons for and against such praise?

SELECTED BIBLIOGRAPHY

Beard, James. (ed.) *The Letters and Journals of James Fenimore Cooper,* 2 Vols. Cambridge, Mass: Harvard University Press, 1960.

Bewley, Marius. *The Eccentric Design: Form in the Classic American Novel,* New York: Columbia University Press, 1959.

Boynton, Henry W. *James Fenimore Cooper,* New York: Appleton-Century Company, 1931.

Clemens, Samuel L. (Mark Twain). *How to Tell a Story and Other Essays,* "Fenimore Cooper's Literary Offenses." New York: Harper and Brothers, 1897.

Cooper, James Fenimore (grandson of the novelist) (ed.). *Correspondence of James Fenimore Cooper.* 2 Vols. New Haven, Conn,: Yale University Press, 1922.

Grossman, James. *James Fenimore Cooper,* New York: William Sloan Associates, Inc.; London: Methuen & Co., Ltd., 1949.

Lawrence, D. H. *Studies in Classic American Literature,* New York: Doubleday & Company, 1961.

Lewis, R. W. B. *The American Adam: Innocence, Tragedy and Tradition in the Nineteenth Century,* Chicago: University of Chicago Press, 1956.

Ringe, Donald A. *James Fenimore Cooper,* New York: Twayne Publishers, 1961.

Spiller, Robert E. *Fenimore Cooper: Critic of his Time,* New York: Minton, Balch & Co., 1931.

Walker, Warren S. *James Fenimore Cooper,* New York: Barnes and Noble, Inc., 1962.